Table of Contents

 W9-CAF-675

Read the rhyme aloud. Then say, "This is a square. It has four sides, all the same length." Ask the child to color the row of squares. Then ask him or her to use a finger to trace the first square in the bottom row, and a pencil to trace and draw the next two squares in that row.

Square

> **A, B, C, Tumble-Down D**
> A, B, C, tumble-down D,
> The cat's in the cupboard
> And can't see me!

Color.

Trace and draw.

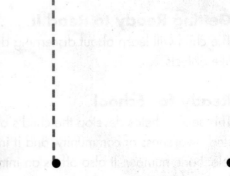

Understanding shapes: recognizing shape names

Read the rhyme aloud. Then say, "This is a circle. It is round." Ask the child to color the row of circles. Then ask him or her to use a finger to trace the first circles in the bottom row, and a pencil to trace and draw the next two circles in that row.

Circle

Hickory, Dickory, Dock
Hickory, dickory, dock!
The mouse ran up the clock.
The clock struck one, the mouse ran down,
Hickory, dickory, dock.

Color.

Trace and draw.

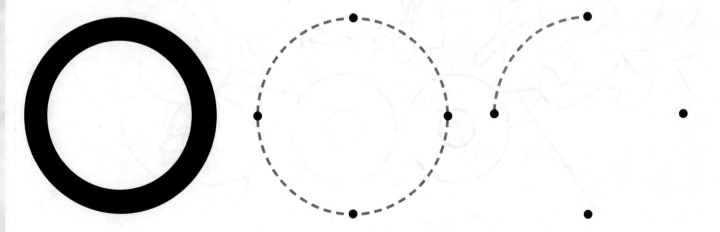

Ask the child to point to all the circles and then color them.

Round World

Color the ⭘s.

Understanding shapes

Ask the child to point to all the squares and then color them.

Square World

Color the ☐s.

Before the child begins coloring, point to the words *large* and *small* and discuss their meaning. Then proceed with the activity.

Large and Small

Color what is **large.**

Color what is **small.**

Understanding sizes and size words

Before the child begins coloring, point to the words *long* and *short* and discuss their meaning. Then proceed with the activity.

Long and Short

Color what is **long.**

Color what is **short.**

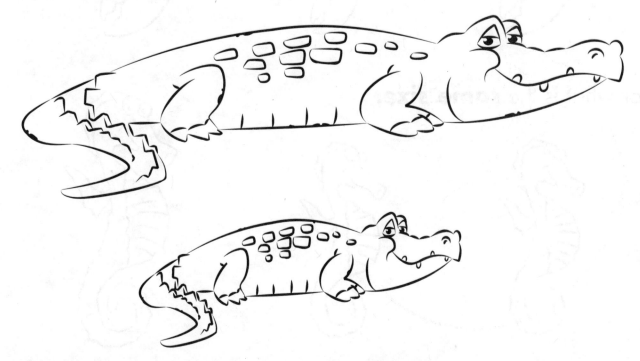

As the child looks at the fish pictures ask: "How are these fish different? How are they the same?" Then proceed with the rest of the page.

Same Size

Color what is the **same size.**

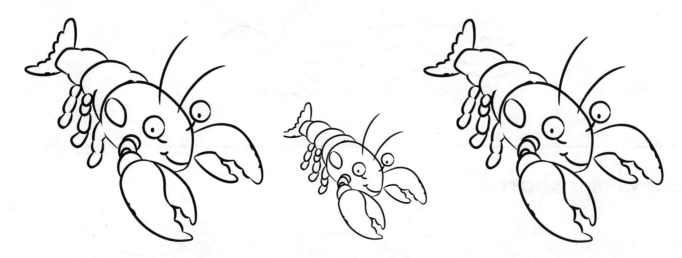

Color what is the **same size.**

Understanding sizes and size words

Read the rhyme aloud. Then say, "This pie slice is a triangle. It has three sides." Ask the child to color the row of triangles. Then ask him or her to use a finger to trace the first triangle in the bottom row, and a pencil to trace and draw the next two triangles in that row.

Triangle

Simple Simon
Simple Simon met a pie man,
Going to the fair;
Says Simple Simon to the pie man,
"Let me taste your ware."

Color.

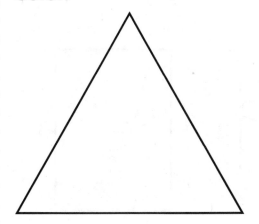
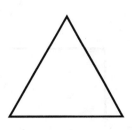
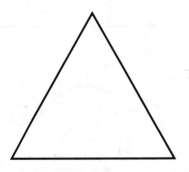

Trace and draw.

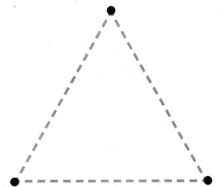

Understanding shapes: recognizing shape names

Read the rhyme aloud. Then say, "This door is a rectangle. It has four sides—but two sides are long and two are short."
Ask the child to color the row of rectangles. Then ask him or her to use a finger to trace the first rectangle in the bottom
row, and a pencil to trace and draw the next two rectangles in that row.

Rectangle

Mary at the Cottage Door
One, two, three, four,
Mary at the cottage door;
Five, six, seven, eight,
Eating cherries off a plate.

Color.

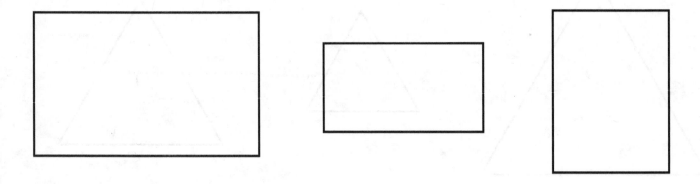

Trace and draw.

10   Understanding shapes: recognizing shape names

Ask the child to point to all the rectangles in the picture and then color them.

Find the Rectangles!

Color the ☐ s.

Understanding shapes

11

Triangle Fun

Color the △ s.

Understanding shapes

Read the rhyme aloud. Point to the picture of two wheat stalks and ask the child tell which is long and which is short. Then proceed with the rest of the page.

Long and Small

Oats and Beans and Barley
Oats and beans and barley grow,
Oats and beans and barley grow.
Do you or I or anyone know,
How oats and beans and barley grow?

Color what is **long.**

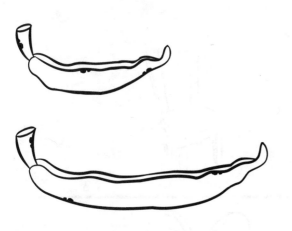
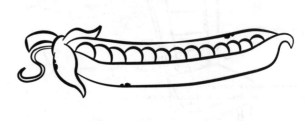

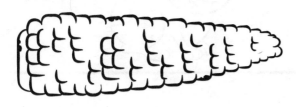

Big and Little

little   **big**

> ### Pussycat, Pussycat
> Pussycat, Pussycat, where have you been?
> I've been to London to visit the Queen.
> Pussycat, Pussycat, what did you there?
> I frightened a little mouse under her chair.

Color what is **big.** Circle what is **little.**

14

Understanding sizes and size words

Read the rhyme aloud. Ask the child to point to the tall girl and then to the short girl. Then proceed with the rest of the page.

Tall and Short

> ### Mary, Mary
> Mary, Mary quite contrary
> How does your garden grow?
> With silver bells and cockle shells,
> And pretty maids all in a row.

tall

short

Color what is **short**. Circle what is **tall**.

Understanding sizes and size words

Longest and Shortest

Cackle, Cackle
Cackle, cackle, Mother Goose,
Have you any feathers loose?
Truly have I, pretty fellow,
Half enough to fill a pillow.

Color what is **longest.** Circle what is **shortest.**

Read the rhyme aloud. Ask the child to point to the biggest and then to the littlest pig.
Then proceed with the rest of the page.

Shapes and Sizes

Biggest and Littlest

To Market, To Market
To market, to market,
To buy a fat pig;
Home again, home again,
Jiggety-jig.

Color what is **biggest.**
Circle what is **littlest.**

Understanding sizes and size words

Tallest and Shortest

I'm a Little Teapot
I'm a little teapot, short and stout.
Here is my handle, here is my spout.
When I get all steamed up, then I shout:
"Tip me over and pour me out!"

Color what is **tallest.**
Circle what is **shortest.**

Understanding shapes: recognizing shape names

[1] Ask the child to color each playing card and cut it out along the dotted lines. [2] Place all cards face up. Point to one and ask the child to say whether it shows the biggest, smallest or middle-sized jacket. Ask the child to find the other two jackets that match in size. [3] Lay all cards face down. In turn, each player flips over two cards. If the cards show the jacket in different sizes, the player returns the cards to their original places, face down. If the two cards picked show the jacket in the same size, the player keeps the cards and takes a second turn. Play ends when one player has three matches.

Same Size Match-up

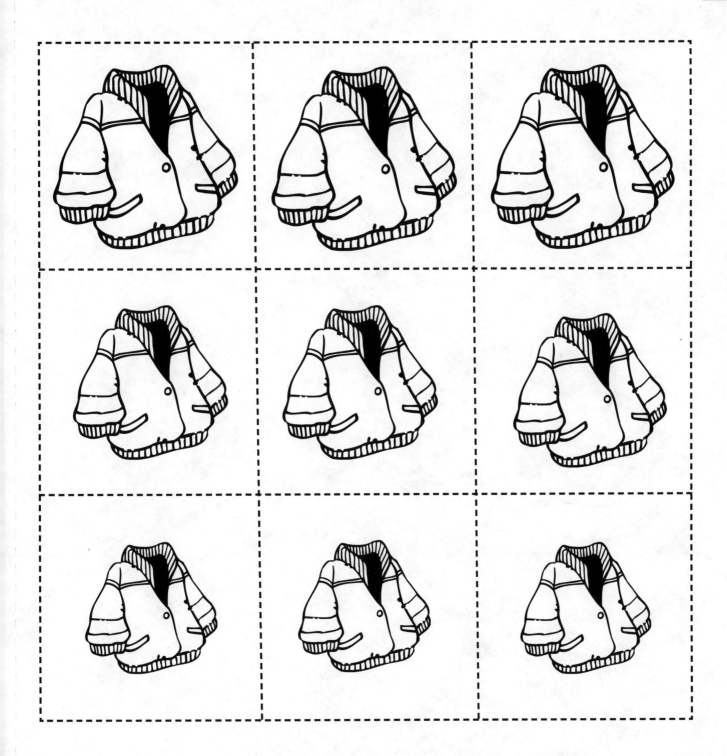

Understanding sizes and size words

19

Read the rhyme aloud. Then read each of the directions below and ask the child to complete the activities.

Shapes and Sizes

Size Review

Pat-a-Cake
Pat-a-cake, pat-a-cake, baker's man!
Bake me a cake as fast as you can;
Roll it and pat it and mark it with a B,
And put it in the oven for baby and me.

Color the **short** pitcher.

Color the **big** cupcake.

Color the **long** spoon.

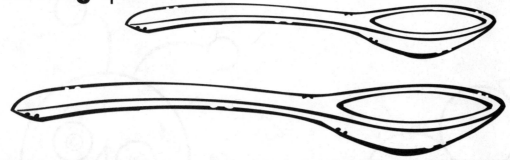

Color the **biggest** pie.

Circle & Caterpillar

Trace the 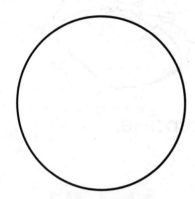 s.

circle

Color only the ◯ s.

Recognizing shapes; tracing circles

Square & Train

Trace the ☐ s.

square

Color only the ☐ s.

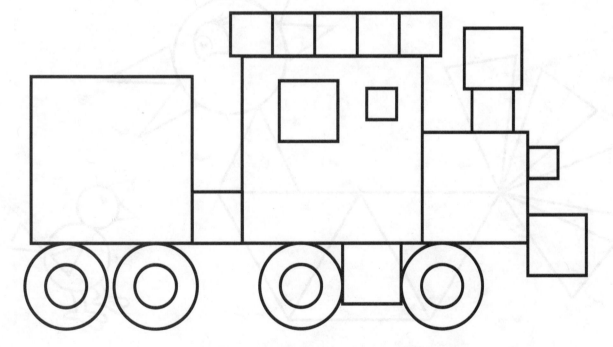

Recognizing shapes; tracing squares

Triangle & Bird

Trace the 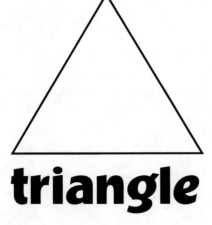s.

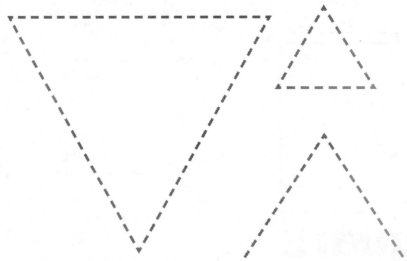

triangle

Color only the △s.

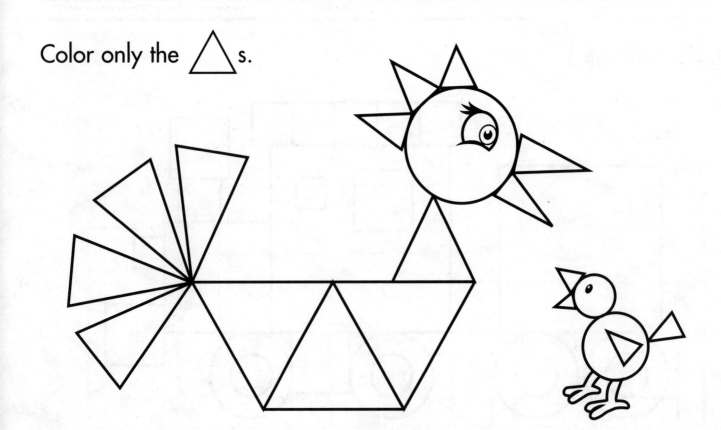

Recognizing shapes; tracing triangles

Rectangle & House

Trace the ☐ s.

rectangle

Color only the ☐ s.

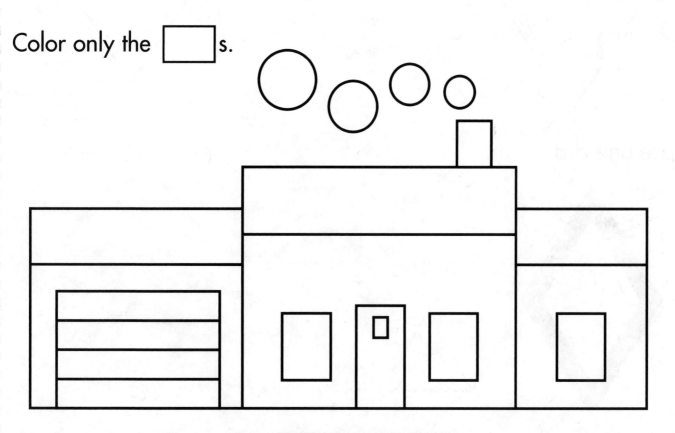

Read the rhyme aloud. Point to the diamond and say, "This is a diamond." Ask the child to color the row of diamonds. Then ask him or her to use a finger to trace the first diamond in the bottom row, and a pencil to trace and draw the next two diamonds in that row.

Diamond

> ## Little Girl
> Little girl, little girl, where have you been?
> Gathering roses to give to the queen.
> Little girl, little girl, what gave she you?
> She gave me a diamond as big as my shoe.

Color the 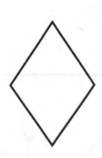s.

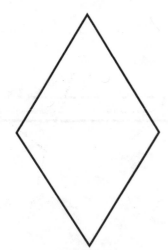

Trace and draw.

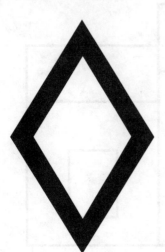 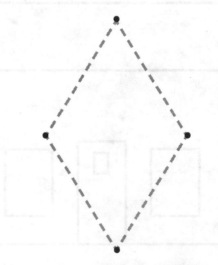 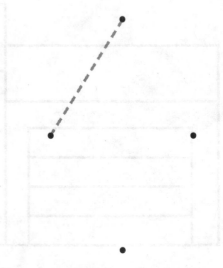

Understanding shapes; recognizing shape names

Read the rhyme aloud. Point to the star and say, "Do you know this shape? It's a star." Ask the child to color the row of stars. Then ask him or her to use a finger to trace the first star in the bottom row, and a pencil to trace and draw the next two stars in that row.

Star

Star Light, Star Bright
Star light, star bright
The first star I see tonight;
I wish I may, I wish I might
Have the wish I wish tonight.

Color the s.

Trace and draw.

 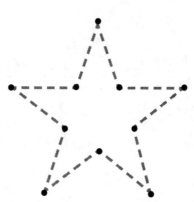 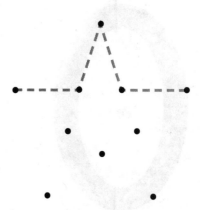

Read the rhyme aloud. Point to the oval and say, "This shape is called an oval. It looks like an egg." Ask the child to color the row of ovals. Then ask him or her to use a finger to trace the first oval in the bottom row, and a pencil to trace and draw the next two ovals in that row.

Oval

Humpty Dumpty
Humpty Dumpty sat on a wall,
Humpty Dumpty had a great fall;
All the king's horses and all the king's men
Couldn't put Humpty together again.

Color the ⬭s.

  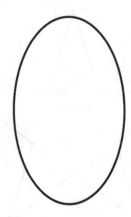

Trace and draw.

 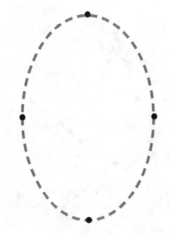 

Understanding shapes; recognizing shape names

Read the rhyme aloud. Point to the heart and say, "Do you know the name of this shape? It's a heart." Ask the child to color the row of hearts. Then ask him or her to use a finger to trace the first heart in the bottom row, and a pencil to trace and draw the next two hearts in that row.

Heart

Heart Tarts
The Queen of Hearts made some tarts,
All on a summer's day.
The Jack of Hearts ate the tarts,
Then put away the tray.

Color the ♡s.

Trace and draw.

Understanding shapes; recognizing shape names

Ask the child to name the shapes in the first row. Then ask, "Which shape comes next?" Ask the child to draw the next shape in the empty box and color the row of shapes as indicated. Repeat for each row.

Next Shape?

 = ☆   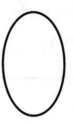 = ⬭

   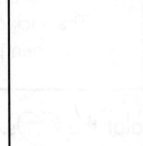

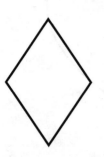 = ◇    = ♡

 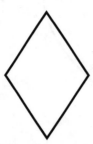  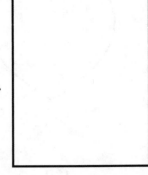

 = ⬭    = ◇

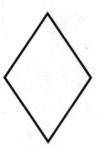 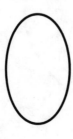 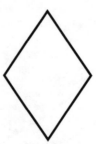 

Recognizing and continuing patterns; drawing shapes

Ask the child to color the picture according to the color key.

Color Choo-Choo

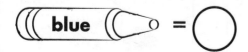 = ◯

 = ☐

red = △

 = ▭

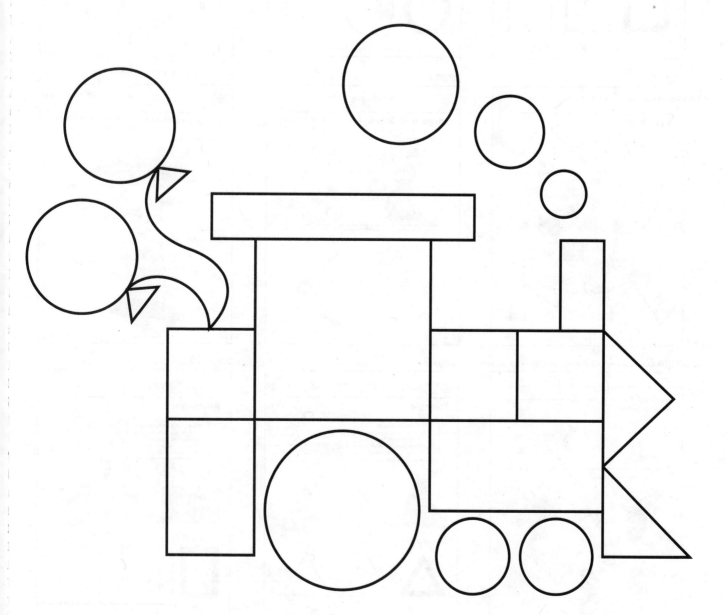

Distinguishing among basic shapes; following directions

31

Answer Key

As the child completes the pages in this section, review his or her answers. When you take the time to correct the work and explain mistakes, you're showing your child that you feel learning is important.

page 2

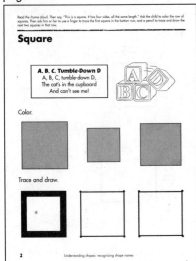

page 3

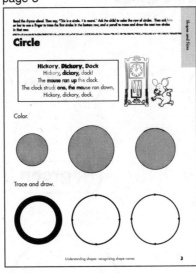

page 4

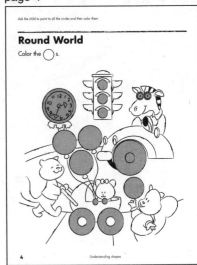

page 5

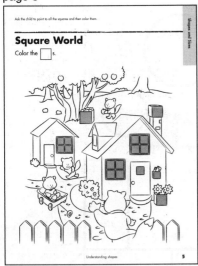

page 6

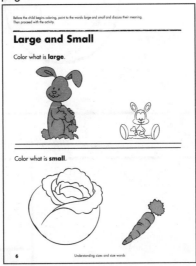

page 7

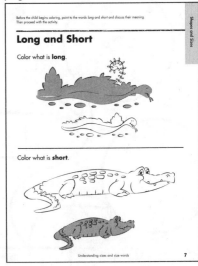

page 8

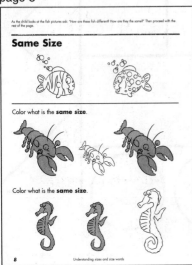

page 9

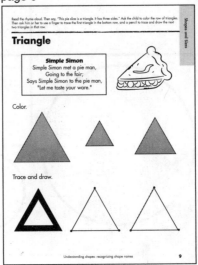

page 10

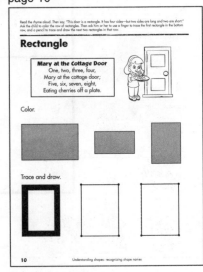

page 11

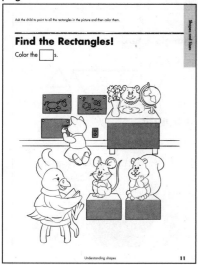

page 12

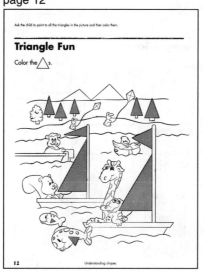

page 13

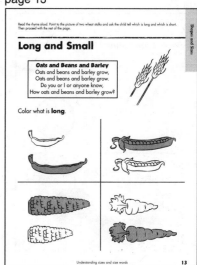

page 14

page 15

page 16

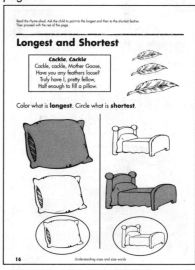

page 17

page 18

page 21

Answers

33

Circle & Caterpillar

Trace the ◯s.

circle

Color only the ◯s.

22   Recognizing shapes; tracing circles

Shapes and Sizes

Square & Train

Trace the ▢s.

square

Color only the ▢s.

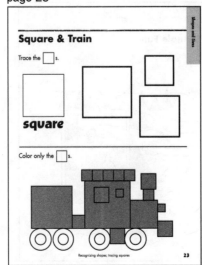

Recognizing shapes; tracing squares   23

Triangle & Bird

Trace the △s.

triangle

Color only the △s.

24   Recognizing shapes; tracing triangles

Rectangle & House

Trace the ▭s.

rectangle

Color only the ▭s.

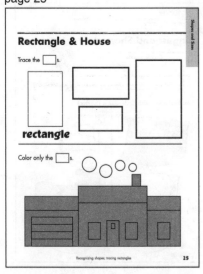

Recognizing shapes; tracing rectangles   25

Read the rhyme aloud. Point to the diamond and say, "This is a diamond." Ask the child to color the row of diamonds. Then ask him or her to use a finger to trace the first diamond in the bottom row, and a pencil to trace and draw the next two diamonds in that row.

Diamond

Little Girl
Little girl, little girl, where have you been?
Gathering roses to give to the queen.
Little girl, little girl, what gave she you?
She gave me a diamond as big as my shoe.

Color the ◇s.

Trace and draw.

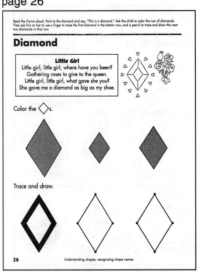

26   Understanding shapes; recognizing shape names

Read the rhyme aloud. Point to the star and say, "Do you know this shape? It's a star." Ask the child to color the row of stars. Then ask him or her to use a finger to trace the first star in the bottom row, and a pencil to trace and draw the next two stars in that row.

Shapes and Sizes

Star

Star Light, Star Bright
Star light, star bright
The first star I see tonight;
I wish I may, I wish I might
Have the wish I wish tonight.

Color the ☆s.

Trace and draw.

Understanding shapes; recognizing shape names   27

Read the rhyme aloud. Point to the oval and say, "This shape is called an oval. It looks like an egg." Ask the child to color the row of ovals. Then ask him or her to use a finger to trace the first oval in the bottom row, and a pencil to trace and draw the next two ovals in that row.

Oval

Humpty Dumpty
Humpty Dumpty sat on a wall,
Humpty Dumpty had a great fall;
All the king's horses and all the king's men
Couldn't put Humpty together again.

Color the ◯s.

Trace and draw.

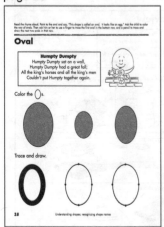

28   Understanding shapes; recognizing shape names

Read the rhyme aloud. Point to the heart and say, "Do you know the name of this shape? It's a heart." Ask the child to color the row of hearts. Then ask him or her to use a finger to trace the first heart in the bottom row, and a pencil to trace and draw the next two hearts in that row.

Shapes and Sizes

Heart

Heart Tarts
The Queen of Hearts made some tarts,
All on a summer's day.
The Jack of Hearts ate the tarts,
Then put away the tray.

Color the ♡s.

Trace and draw.

Understanding shapes; recognizing shape names   29

Ask the child to name the shapes in the first row. Then ask, "Which shape comes next?" Ask the child to draw the next shape in the empty box and color the row of shapes as indicated. Repeat for each row.

Next Shape?

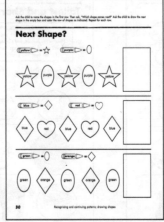

30   Recognizing and continuing patterns; drawing shapes

Ask the child to color the picture according to the color key.

Shapes and Sizes

Color Choo-Choo

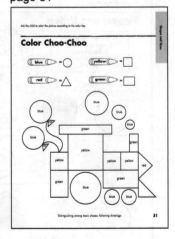

Distinguishing among basic shapes; following directions   31

Same Amount

Match.

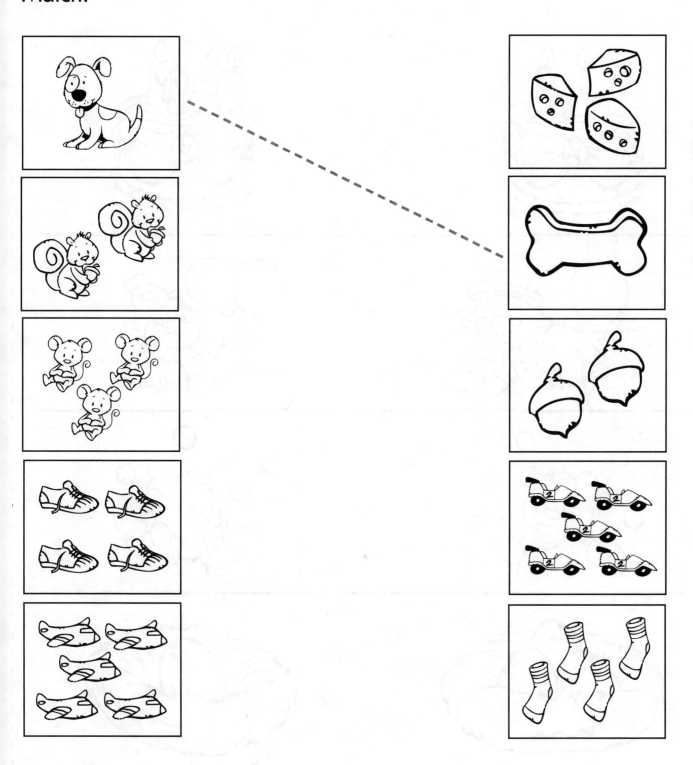

More

Color the one with **more.**

Fewer

Circle the group with **fewer.**

One

Color **one** hippo.
Color **one** bird.
Color the rest of the picture.

Trace.

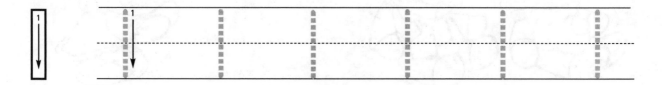

Understanding numbers and number words: counting and printing

Two

2 **two**

Color **two** clowns.

Trace.

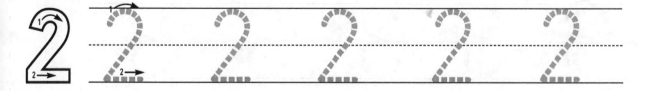

Three

3 three

Color **three** jack-in-the-boxes.

Trace.

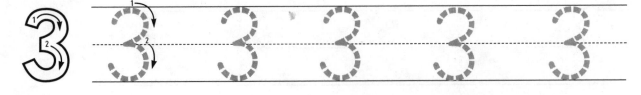

Four

4 four

Color **four** sweaters.

Trace.

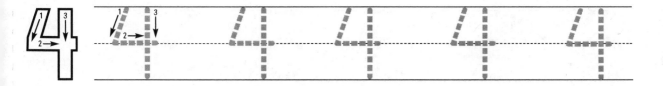

Five

5 five

Color **five** jack-o-lanterns.

Trace.

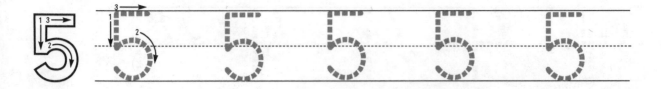

Understanding numbers and number words: counting and printing

Color by Number

Color the paint cans.

1 RED
2 BLUE
3 GREEN
4 YELLOW
5 ORANGE

Understanding numbers

Number Review

Match.

Understanding numbers: counting

Counting 1 to 5

1, 2, 3, 4, 5. Little fishes learn to dive.

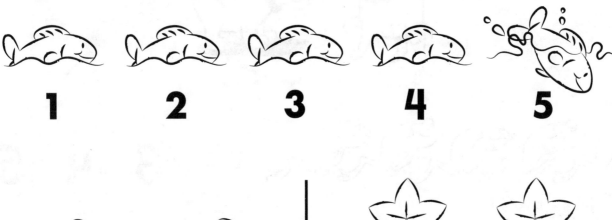

1 **2** **3** **4** **5**

1 **4** **2**

5 **2** **3**

1 **3** **2**

1 **4** **2**

Counting to 5; matching groups of objects and numerals

Ask the child to count how many in each row and circle the number that shows the correct amount.

Small Friends 1 to 5

 3 4 5

 4 2 3

 1 3 2

 3 5 4

Counting to 5; matching groups of objects and numerals

Six

6 **six**

Color **six** dogs.

Trace.

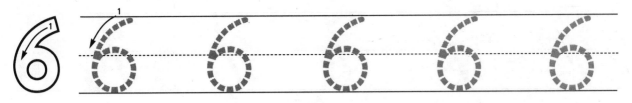

Number Review

Seven

7 **seven**

Circle **seven** grasshoppers.

Trace.

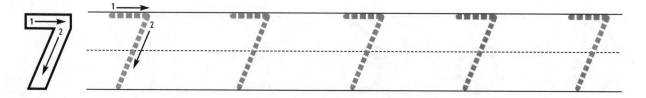

Understanding numbers and number words: counting and printing

Eight

8 **eight**

Color **eight** strawberries.

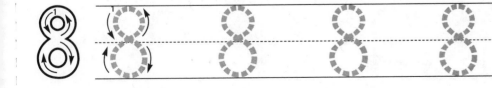

Trace.

8   8   8   8   8

Understanding numbers and number words: counting and printing

49

Nine

9 **nine**

Color **nine** butterflies.

Trace.

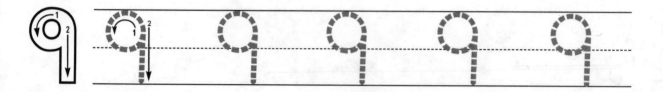

Understanding numbers and number words: counting and printing

Ten

10 ten

Color **ten** cupcakes.

Trace.

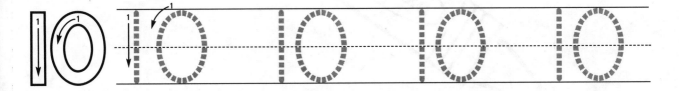

Understanding numbers and number words: counting and printing

Crayon Dot-to-Dot

Connect the dots from **1** to **10**.

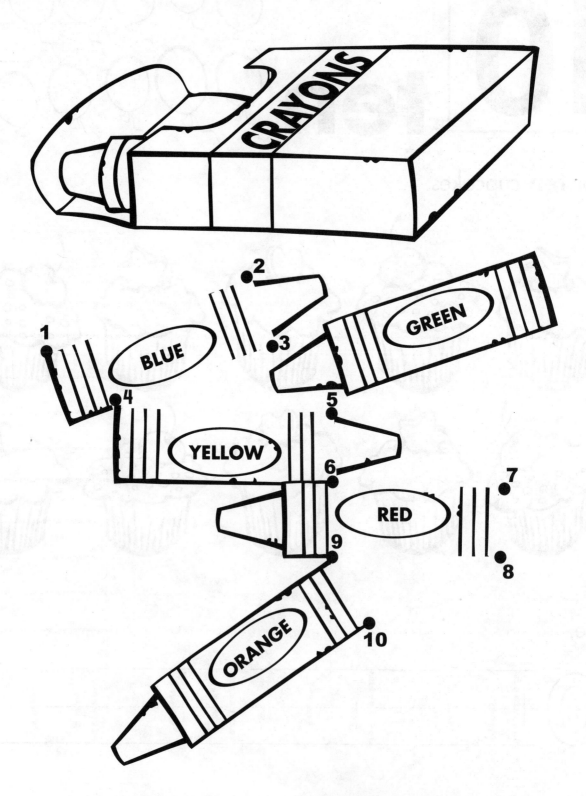

Understanding numerical order; developing fine motor control

Birthdays Count!

Trace.

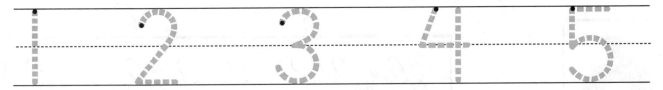

Count how many. Write the number.

Garden Counting

Match.

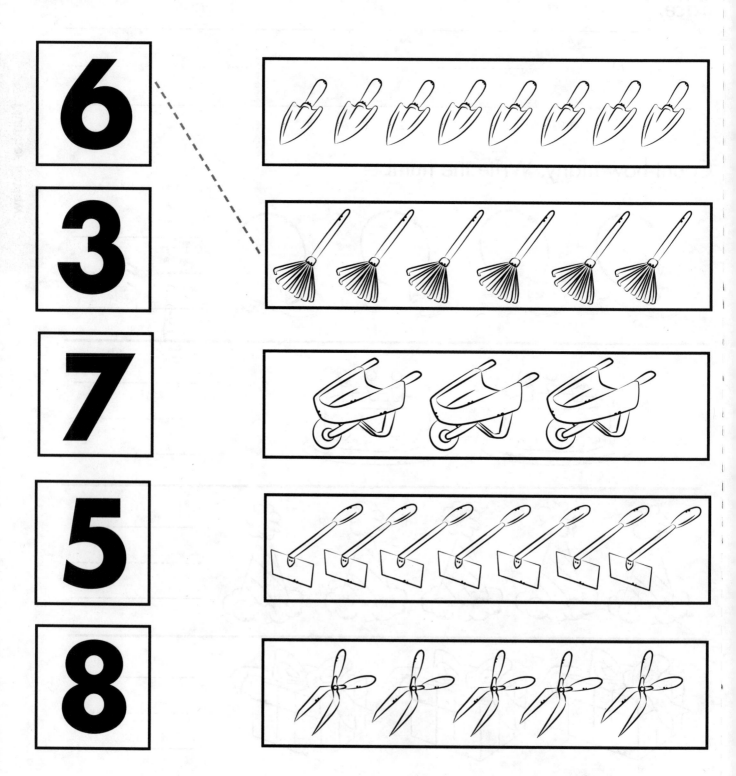

Matching numerals 1 through 8 with correct number of objects

Bus Dot-to-Dot

Connect the dots from **1** to **8**.
Color the picture.

Understanding numerical order; developing fine motor control

Ask the child to say each number aloud. Then ask him or her to count the objects in each row.

1 to 10

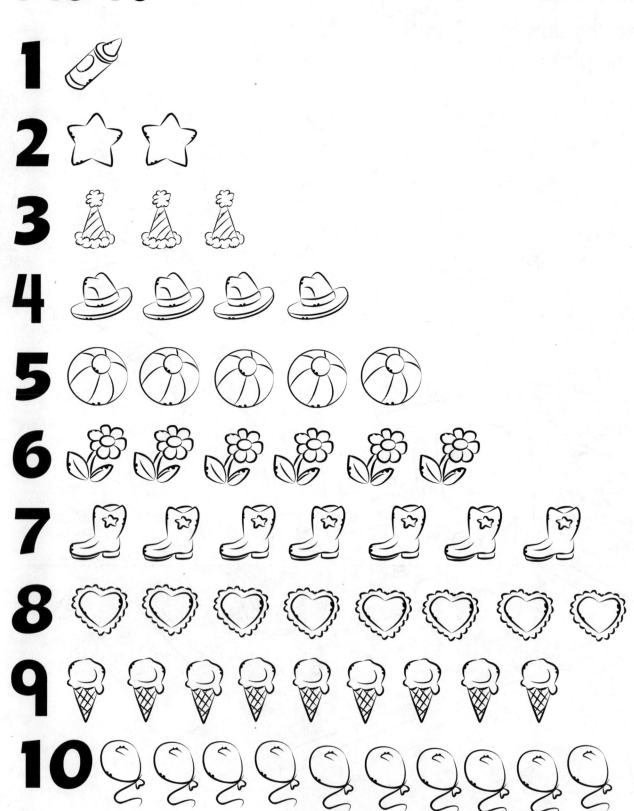

Understanding numbers: counting

Ask the child to count how many objects there are in each box and circle the correct number.

Matching 1 to 10

1   2   3   6   7   8

8   9   10   4   5   6

2   3   4   7   8   9

Matching numerals with corresponding sets of objects

Ask the child to read the number at the left of the first row. Then ask him or her to circle that many rockets. Repeat this procedure for each row.

To the Stars!

4

9

5

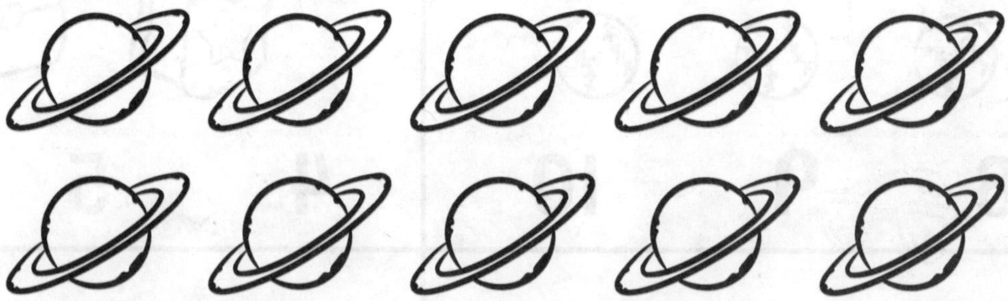

8

Understanding numbers: counting

Ask the child to count how many things there are in each row and write the correct number in the space provided.

Writing 1 to 10

Count from 1 to 10 and 10 to 1 with the child, pointing to the staircase as you count. Then let the child do it on his or her own.

Up to 10 and Down Again!

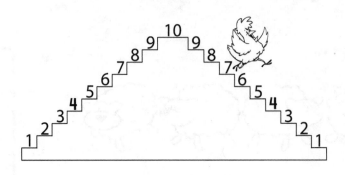

Write **1** to **10**.

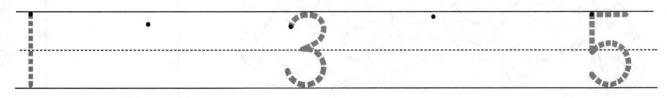

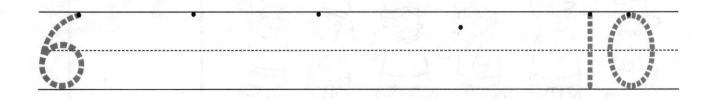

Write **10** to **1**.

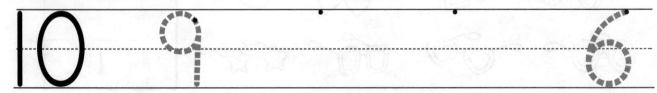

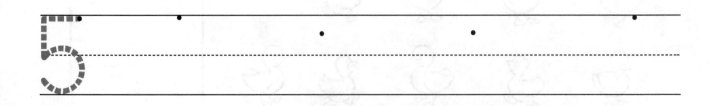

Understanding number order; writing numbers

Point to the first box on the left and ask the child to count the bugs in each stack in that box. Then ask the child to find the box in the right hand column that has the same numbers in the same order, and draw a line between the boxes. Repeat for each box.

Matching Patterns

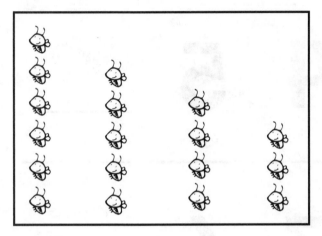

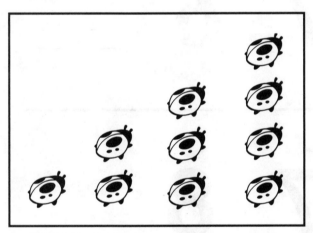

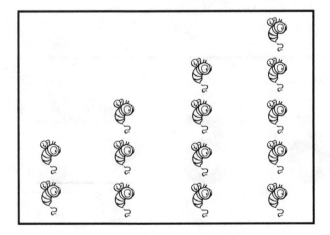

$$1,2,3,4$$

$$2,3,4,5$$

$$6,5,4,3$$

Ask the child to read the first row of numbers, tell what number is needed next and write that number on the line. Then ask the child to read the second row. Tell the child how this pattern is different from that of the first row (the numbers in the second row are in reverse order). Ask the child to write the next number in the pattern. Then ask him or her to read and complete the last two rows.

Number Patterns

1 2 3 4 5 6

10 9 8 7 6 ___

4 5 6 7 8 ___

9 8 7 6 5 ___

Counting forward and backward; recognizing number order

Answer Key

As the child completes the pages in this section, review his or her answers. When you take the time to correct the work and explain mistakes, you're showing your child that you feel learning is important.

page 35

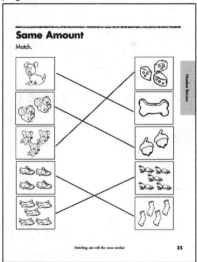

page 36

page 37

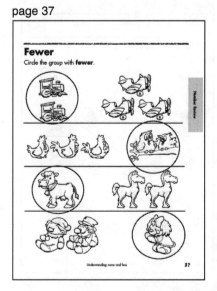

page 38

page 39

page 40

page 41

page 42

page 43

page 44

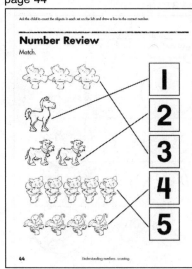

Ask the child to count the objects in each set on the left and draw a line to the correct number.

Number Review
Match.

page 45

As you read each number in the counting rhyme at the top of the page, ask the child to point to a fish. Then ask the child to count the objects in the first box and circle the number that shows the correct amount. Repeat for the next three boxes.

Counting 1 to 5

1, 2, 3, 4, 5. Little fishes learn to dive.

page 46

Ask the child to count how many in each row and circle the number that shows the correct amount.

Small Friends 1 to 5

page 47

Point out the numeral and the number word. Ask the child to say, "six" as he or she points to the number word.

Six

6 six

Color **six** dogs.

Trace.

page 48

Point out the numeral and the number word. Ask the child to say, "seven" as he or she points to the number word.

Seven

7 seven

Circle **seven** grasshoppers.

Trace.

page 49

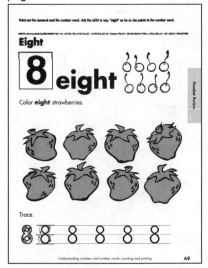

Point out the numeral and the number word. Ask the child to say, "eight" as he or she points to the number word.

Eight

8 eight

Color **eight** strawberries.

Trace.

page 50

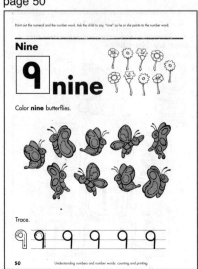

Point out the numeral and the number word. Ask the child to say, "nine" as he or she points to the number word.

Nine

9 nine

Color **nine** butterflies.

Trace.

page 51

Point out the numeral and the number word. Ask the child to say, "ten" as he or she points to the number word.

Ten

10 ten

Color **ten** cupcakes.

Trace.

page 52

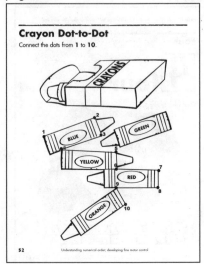

Crayon Dot-to-Dot
Connect the dots from **1** to **10**.

64

Answers

page 53

page 54

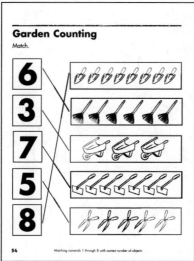

page 55

page 57

page 58

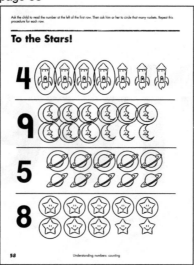

page 59

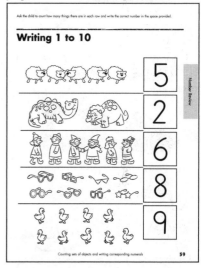

page 60

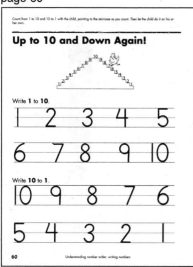

page 61

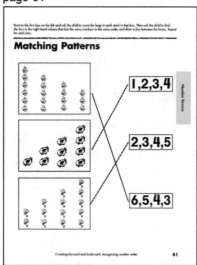

page 62

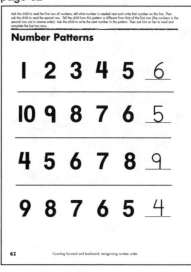

Answers

What Isn't Five?

Matching numerals and number words with amounts

Ask the child to draw an X through each numeral, number word, or group of objects that represents a number different from the other items in the box.

Mixed-up Sets

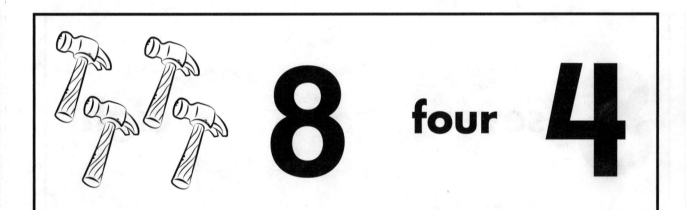

Sorry, Wrong Number

8	seven		eight

10	ten	

Matching numerals and number words with amounts

Ask the child to count the number of objects in each box and circle the correct number word.

Number Words

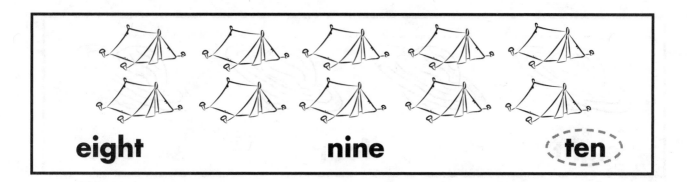

eight nine (ten)

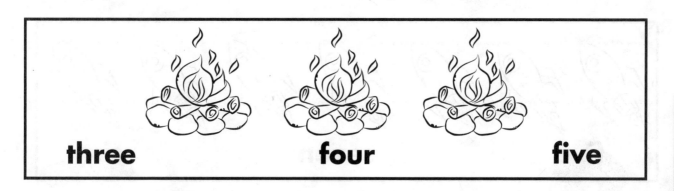

three four five

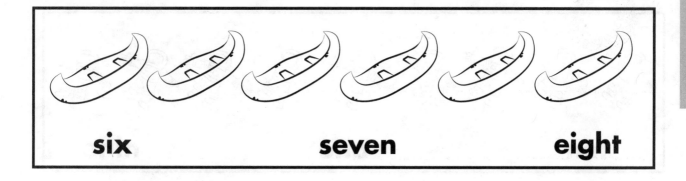

six seven eight

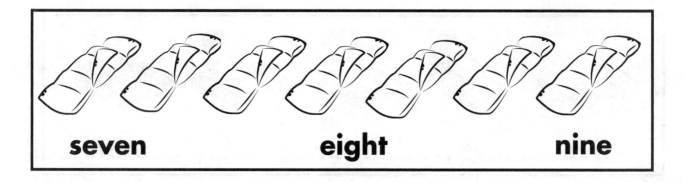

seven eight nine

Sets

More Number Words

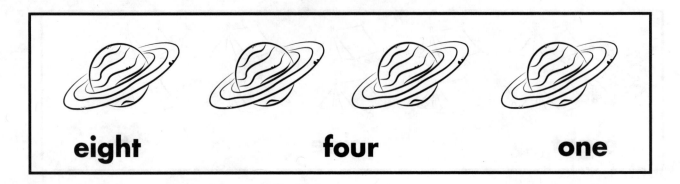

eight   **four**   **one**

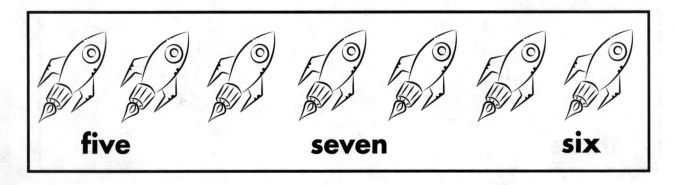

five   **seven**   **six**

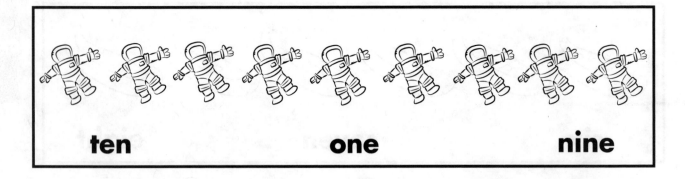

ten   **one**   **nine**

five   **four**   **nine**

In the Garden

1   **2**   **3**   **4**   **5**

Count. Circle the right number.

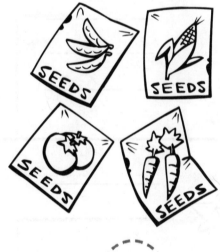

1   (**4**)   **2**

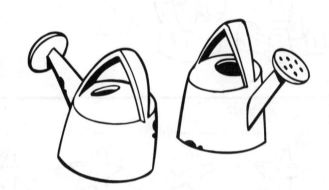

2   **5**   **3**

3   **1**   **5**

2   **4**   **5**

At the Beach

Count. Write how many.

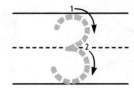

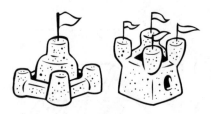

Counting objects and writing numerals 1-5

How Many Toys?

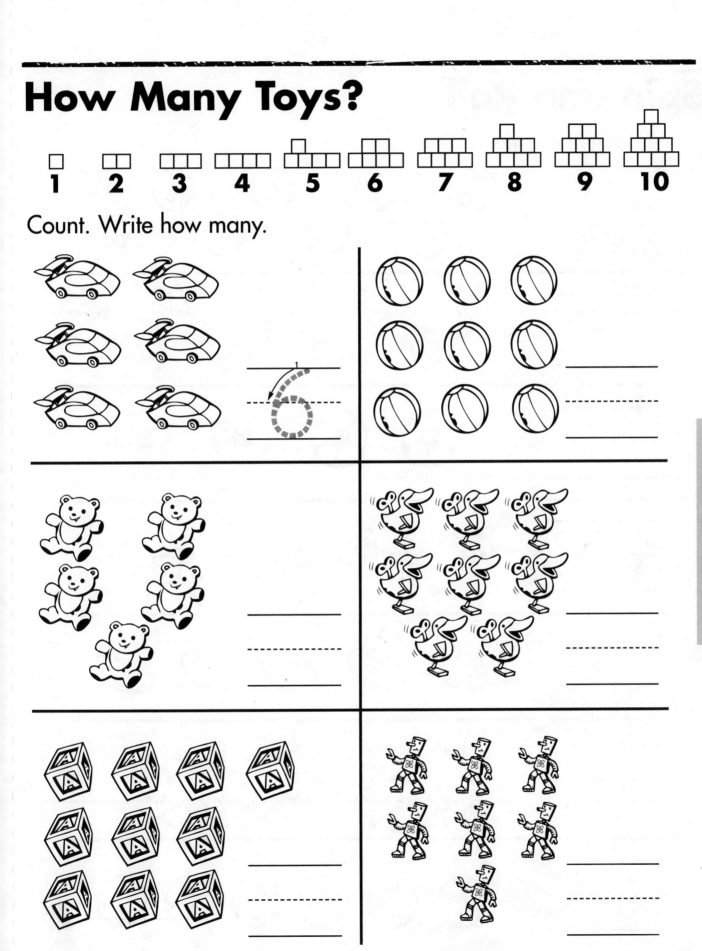

Count. Write how many.

Sets

Spin and Roll

Count. Write how many.

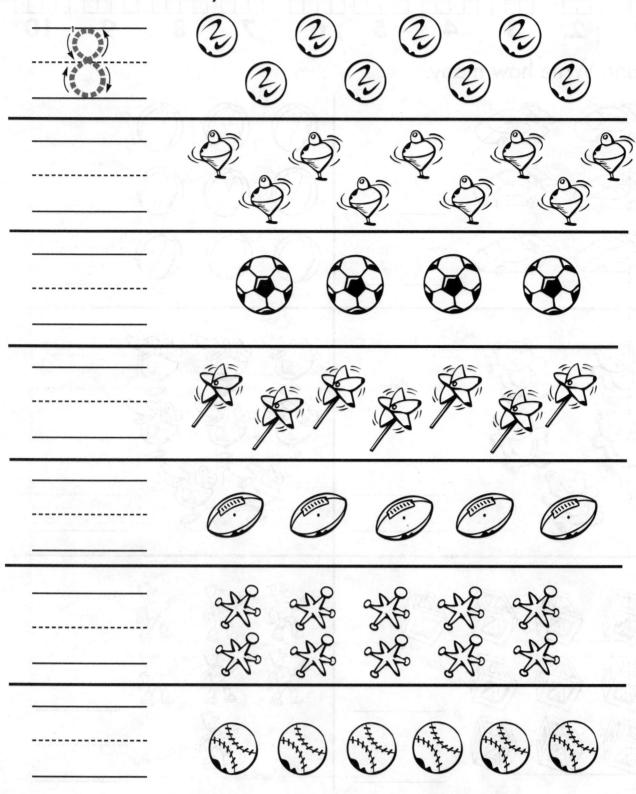

Counting objects and writing numerals to 10

Ask the child to read the number at the left of the first row and then circle that many moons. Repeat the process for the other rows.

In the Sky

9	
7	
5	
10	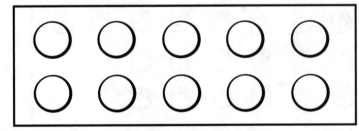
6	
8	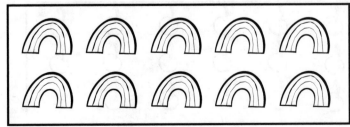

Counting objects and recognizing numerals to 10.

Sweet Treats

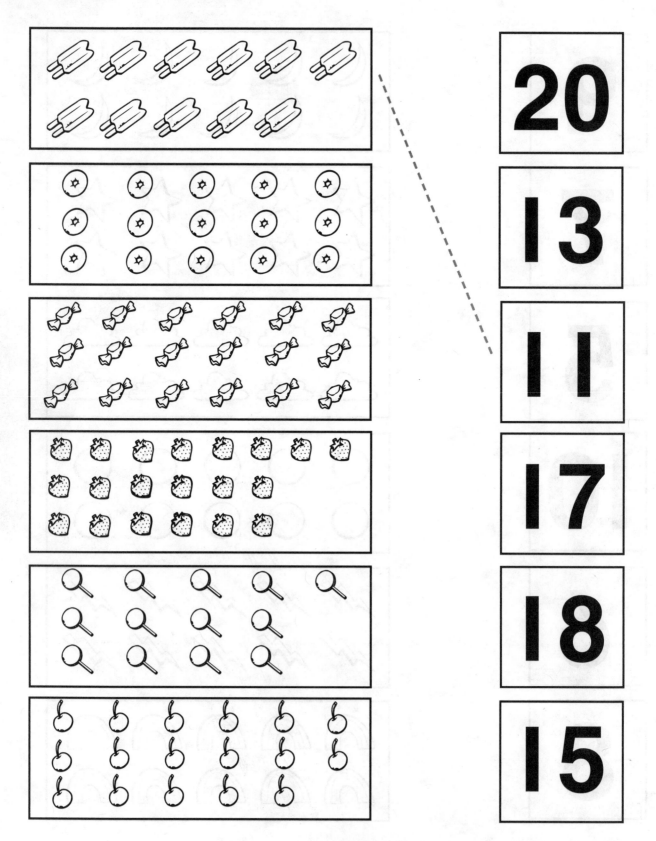

Counting objects and matching numerals 11-20

Ask the child to look at the stacks of pencils at the top of the page. Point out how the some of the pencils in each stack are bound up into sets of ten. Then have the child count the extra pencils in each stack, counting upward from ten.

At School

11 12 13 14 15 16 17 18 19 20

Count. Write how many.

12

_____

_____

_____

_____

_____

_____

_____

Counting Fun

Write the missing numbers.

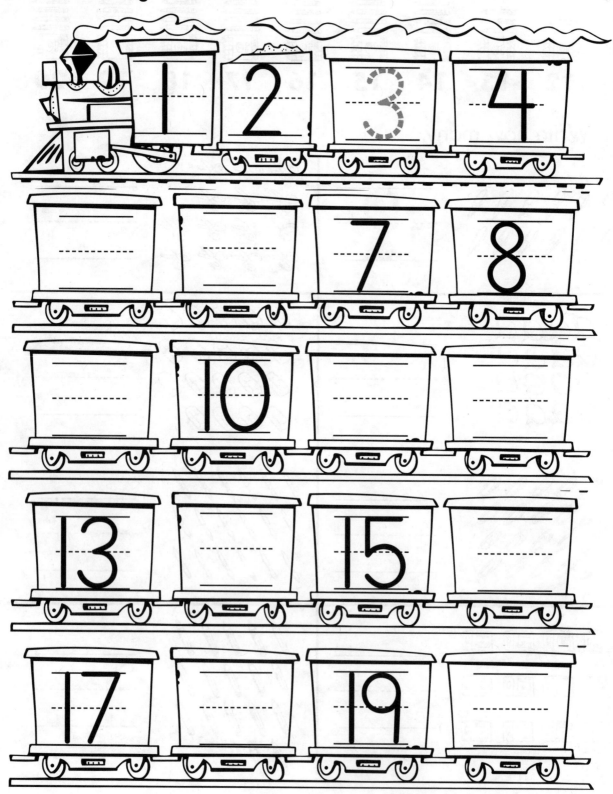

1 2 3 4

__ __ 7 8

__ 10 __ __

13 __ 15 __

17 __ 19 __

Counting objects; writing numerals in sequence through 20

Review

Count. Write how many.

How many 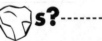**s?** ----------- _____

How many **s?** ----------- _____

How many 🪨**s?** ----------- _____

How many 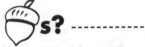**s?** ----------- _____

Sets

Give the Dog a Bone

Match.

Write the answer.

How many 🦴**s do all**

the dogs have together?

_____

- - - - - - - - - - - - - - - - - -

_____

Matching sets showing the same number of objects

More or Less

more   less

Circle the sets that show **more.**

Circle the sets that show **less.**

Sets

One More, One Less

8 is **one more** than 7.
7 is **one less** than 8.

Draw **one more.** Write the number.

How many?

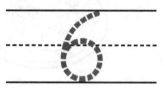

6

How many?

Cross one out to show **one less.** Write the number.

How many?

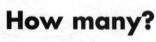

How many?

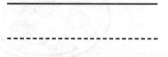

Constructing and recording sets with one more or one less

It's a Party

Circle the sets that show **more.**

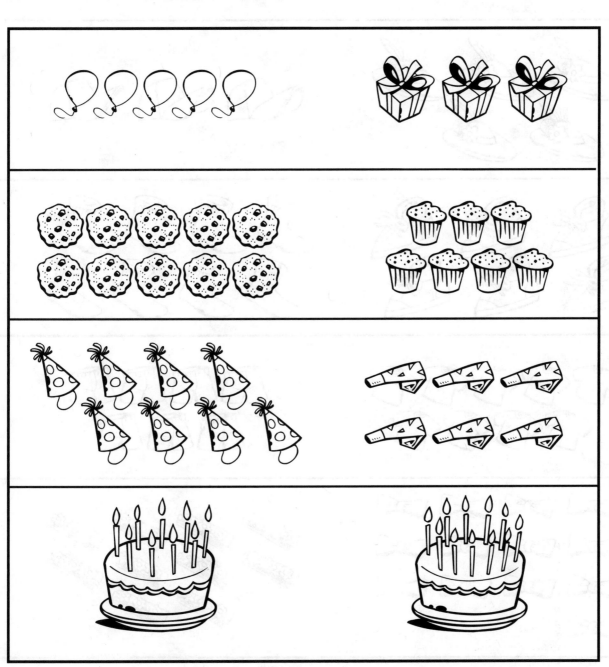

What to Wear?

Circle the sets that show **less.**

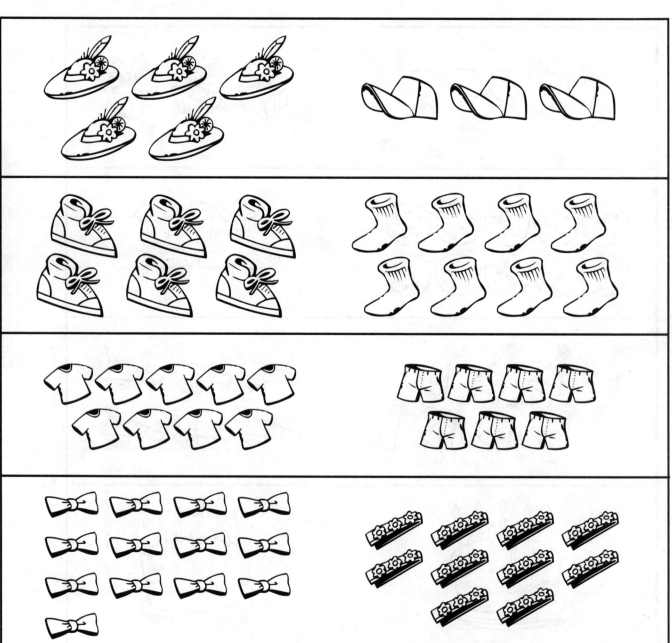

Identifying the number that is more

Counting Flowers

7 is **more** than 4.

Circle the number that is **more.**

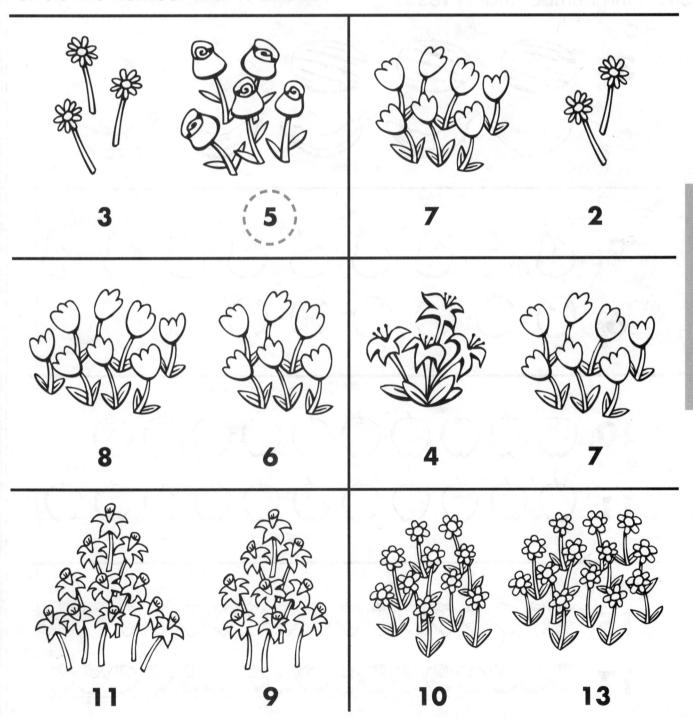

3	(5)	7	2
8	6	4	7
11	9	10	13

Sets

Counting Fruit

6 is **less** than 8.

Circle the number that is **less.**

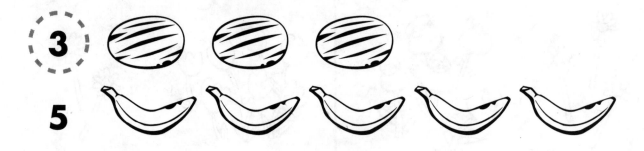

3

5

9

6

10

11

15

17

Identifying the number that is less

What's Before?

1 comes **before** 2.

Write the number that comes **before.**

_____ 9

_____ 6

_____ 4

_____ 12

_____ 16

_____ 3

What's After?

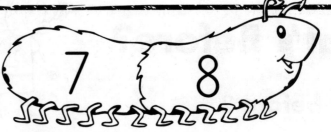

8 comes **after** 7.

Write the number that comes **after**.

6 _____

3 _____

10 _____

16 _____

14 _____

8 _____

12 _____

19 _____

Writing the number that comes after

What's Between?

5 comes **between** 4 and 6.

Write the number that comes **between**.

4
- - - - -
2

11
- - - - -
9

8
- - - - -
6

18
- - - - -
16

15
- - - - -
13

20
- - - - -
18

7
- - - - -
5

Pick It

8 is the **larger** number.
5 is the **smaller** number.

Circle the **larger** number.

2 5	10 8	6 4
15 11	6 9	14 15

Circle the **smaller** number.

10 12	3 5	16 18
7 6	13 19	20 17

Rib-bit Review

What numbers are missing? Write them in.

Draw a ◯ around the number that comes **after** 4.

Draw a **X** over the number that comes **before** 10.

Draw a ☐ around the number that comes **between** 6 and 8.

More Review

Count how many. Write the number.

Box A

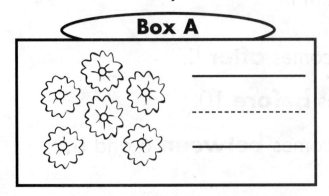

_____
- - - - - - - - - - - -
_____

Box B

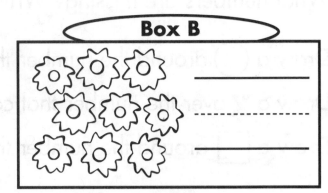

_____
- - - - - - - - - - - -
_____

Box C

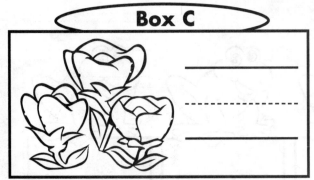

_____
- - - - - - - - - - - -
_____

Box D

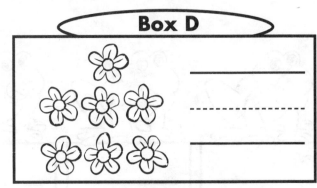

_____
- - - - - - - - - - - -
_____

Box E

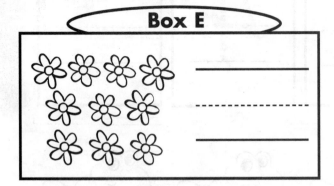

_____
- - - - - - - - - - - -
_____

Box F

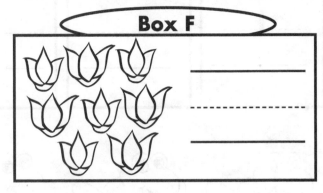

_____
- - - - - - - - - - - -
_____

Circle:

Which box has **more** flowers than the other boxes?   Box A   (Box E)

Which box has **less** flowers than the other boxes?   Box B   Box C

Which box has **one more** flower than box D?   Box F   Box A

Which box has **one less** flower than box B?   Box D   Box F

Writing numerals up to 10; identifying more and less

Answer Key

As the child completes the pages in this section, review his or her answers. When you take the time to correct the work and explain mistakes, you're showing your child that you feel learning is important.

page 66

page 67

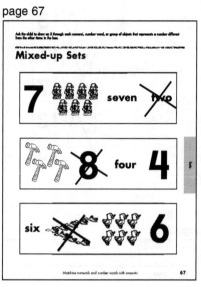

page 68

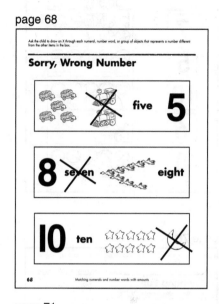

page 69

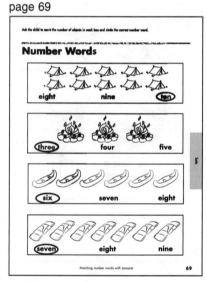

page 70

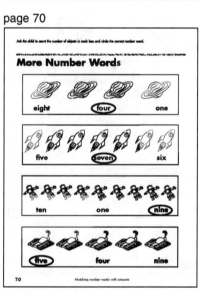

page 71

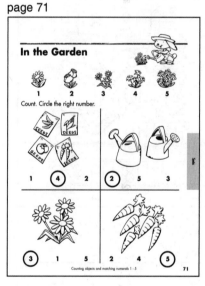

page 72

page 73

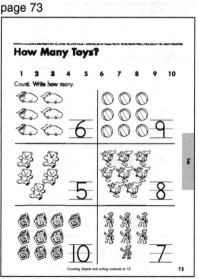

page 74

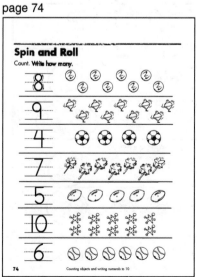

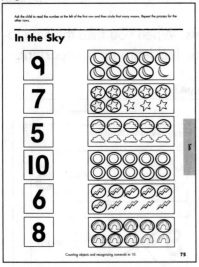

In the Sky

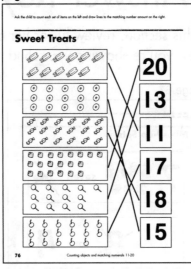

Sweet Treats

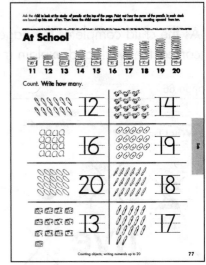

At School

Count. Write how many.

Counting Fun

Write the missing numbers.

Review

Count. Write how many.

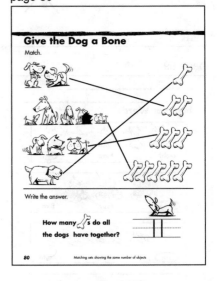

Give the Dog a Bone

Match.

Write the answer.

How many 🦴's do all the dogs have together?

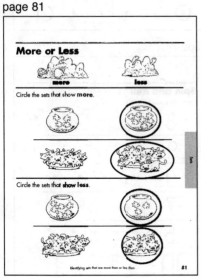

More or Less

Circle the sets that show **more.**

Circle the sets that show **less.**

One More, One Less

Draw **one more.** Write the number.

Cross **one** out to show **one less.** Write the number

It's a Party

Circle the sets that show **more.**

What to Wear?

Circle the sets that show **less**.

84   Identifying the number that is more

Counting Flowers

7 is **more** than 4.

Circle the number that is **more**.

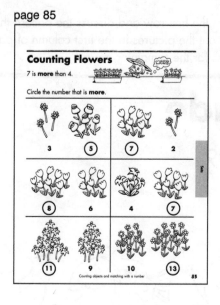

Counting objects and matching with a number   85

Counting Fruit

6 is **less** than 8.

Circle the number that is **less**.

86   Identifying the number that is less

What's Before?

1 comes **before** 2.

Write the number that comes **before**.

Writing the number that comes before   87

What's After?

8 comes **after** 7.

Write the number that comes **after**.

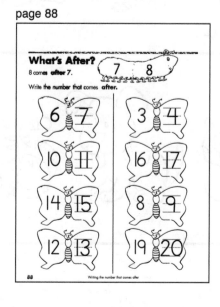

88   Writing the number that comes after

What's Between?

5 comes **between** 4 and 6.

Write the number that comes **between**.

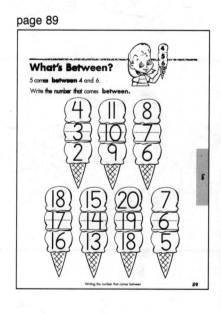

Writing the number that comes between   89

Sets

Pick It

8 is the **larger** number.
5 is the **smaller** number.

Circle the **larger** number.

Circle the **smaller** number.

90   Identifying larger and smaller numbers

After the child has written in the missing numbers, help him or her to understand the remaining directions.

Rib-but Review

What numbers are missing? Write them in.

Draw a ◯ around the number that comes **after** 4.

Draw a **X** over the number that comes **before** 10.

Draw a ☐ around the number that comes **between** 6 and 8.

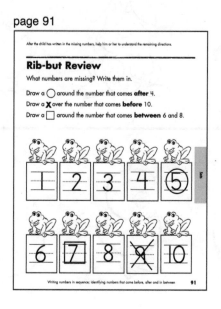

Writing numbers in sequence; Identifying numbers that come before, after and in between   91

More Review

Count how many. Write the number.

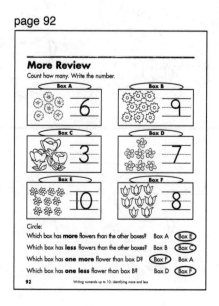

Circle:

Which box has **more** flowers than the other boxes?   Box A   (Box E)

Which box has **less** flowers than the other boxes?   Box B   (Box C)

Which box has **one more** flower than box D?   (Box F)   Box A

Which box has **one less** flower than box B?   Box D   (Box F)

92   Writing numerals up to 10; identifying more and less

Answers

Ask the child to name the animals pictured in the first row and discuss the pattern that the pictures follow. Ask, "Which animal comes next?" Then help the child cut out the pictures in the first column of page 99 and paste the correct picture at the end of the first row. Repeat the process for the remaining rows.

Animal Parade

Use cutouts from page 99.

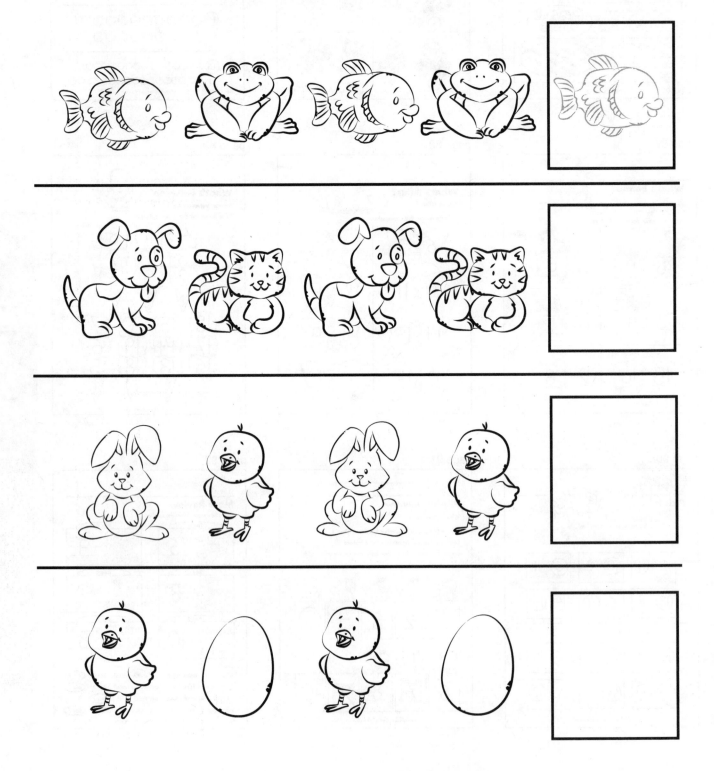

Recognizing and continuing patterns

Ask the child to name the toys pictured in the first row and discuss the pattern that the pictures follow. Ask, "Which toy comes next?" Then help the child cut out the pictures in the second column of page 99 and paste the correct picture at the end of the first row. Repeat the process for the remaining rows.

Toy Parade

Use cutouts from page 99.

Recognizing and continuing patterns

97

Ask the child to name the objects pictured in the first row and discuss the pattern that the pictures follow. Ask, "What comes next—HAT or sweater?" Then help the child cut out the pictures in the third column of page 99 and paste the correct picture at the end of the first row. Repeat the process for the remaining rows.

Clothes on Parade

Use cutouts from page 99.

Recognizing and continuing patterns

Use on page 96.

Use on page 97.

Use on page 98.

In each row, help the child read the crayon color above each picture and color accordingly. Then discuss the "color pattern" of the row to help the child decide which color to use on the last picture.

Color Patterns

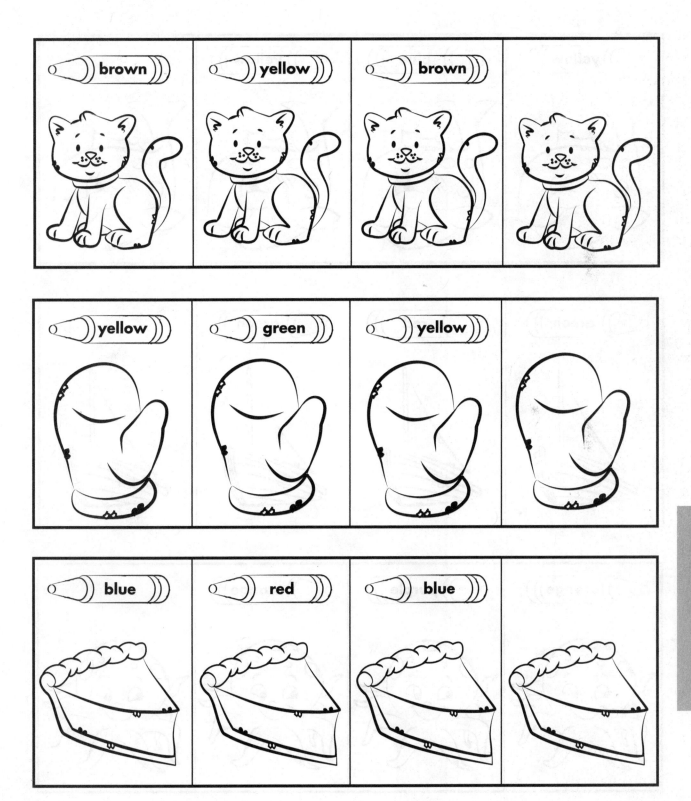

Patterns

In each row, help the child read the crayon color above each picture and color accordingly. Then discuss the "color pattern" of the row to help the child decide which color to use on the last picture.

Sea Colors

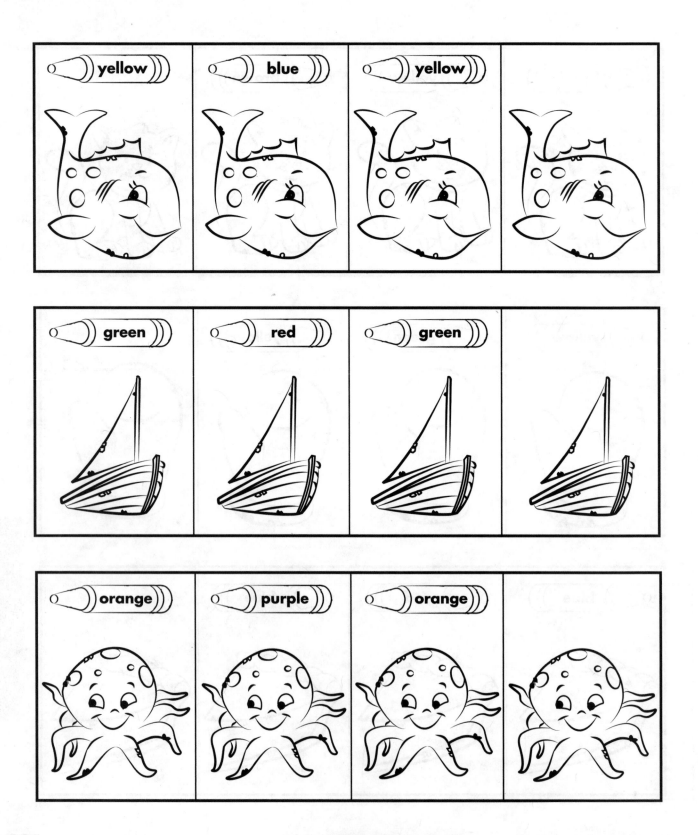

Recognizing and continuing patterns

Ask the child to draw the shape that continues the pattern in each row. Then ask him or her to color each completed row according to the color printed on the crayon above the row. Next, ask the child to name the colored shapes in each row aloud, such as "Red triangle, red circle, red triangle, red circle."

One-color Patterns

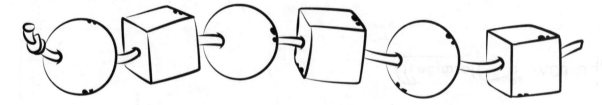

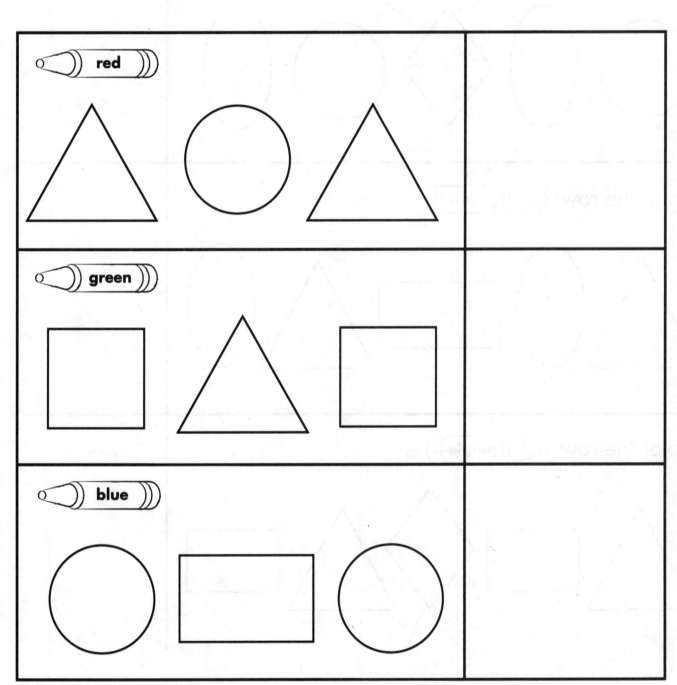

Patterns

Ask the child to draw the shape that continues the pattern in each row. Then ask the child to color the row according to the color directions above it. Next, ask the child to name the colored shapes in each row aloud, such as "Orange circle, orange oval, orange diamond, orange circle, orange oval, orange diamond."

More One-color Patterns

Color the row ⬡orange.

Color the row ⬡yellow.

Color the row ⬡purple.

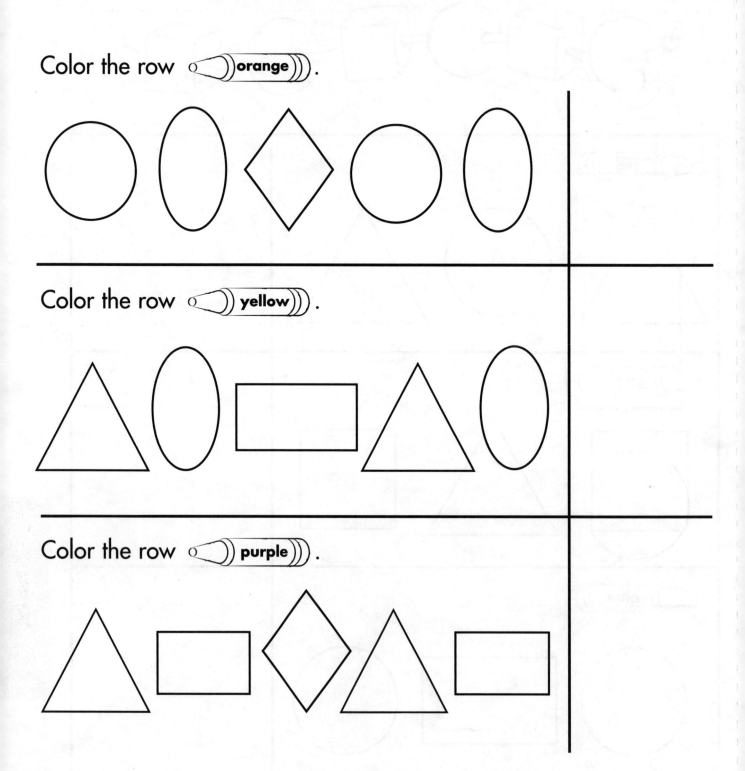

Recognizing and continuing patterns

Ask the child to draw the shape that continues the pattern in each row. Then ask the child to use the color key to color the shapes. Once completed, ask the child to name each shape and color aloud, such as "Green square, yellow circle, green square, yellow circle."

Two-color Patterns

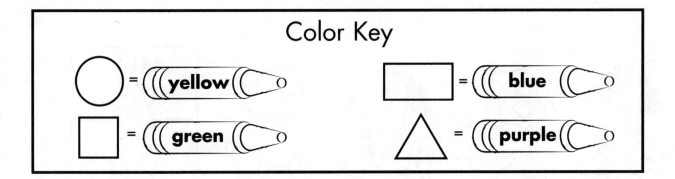

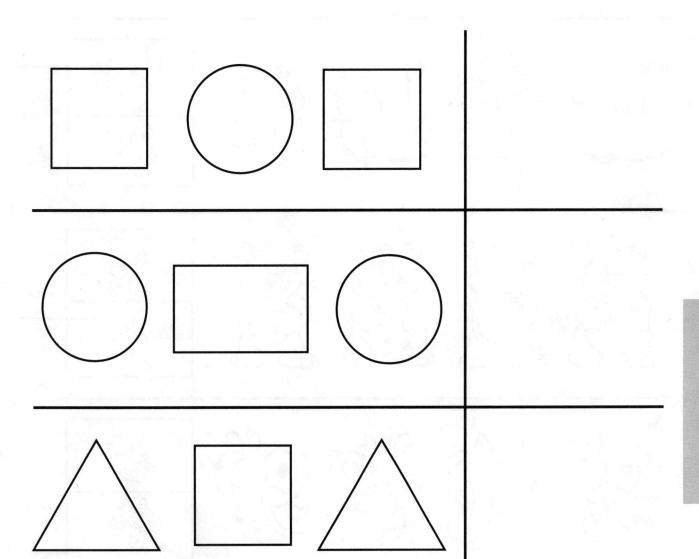

Recognizing and continuing patterns

105

Animal Patterns

Circle what comes next.

Recognizing and continuing patterns

Ask the child to draw the shape that continues the pattern in each row. Then ask the child to color the shapes according to the color word printed on each of them and continue the color pattern for the shape he or she drew. Once completed, ask the child to name each colored shape aloud, such as "Green diamond, orange triangle, yellow circle, green diamond, orange triangle, yellow circle."

Colored Shape Patterns

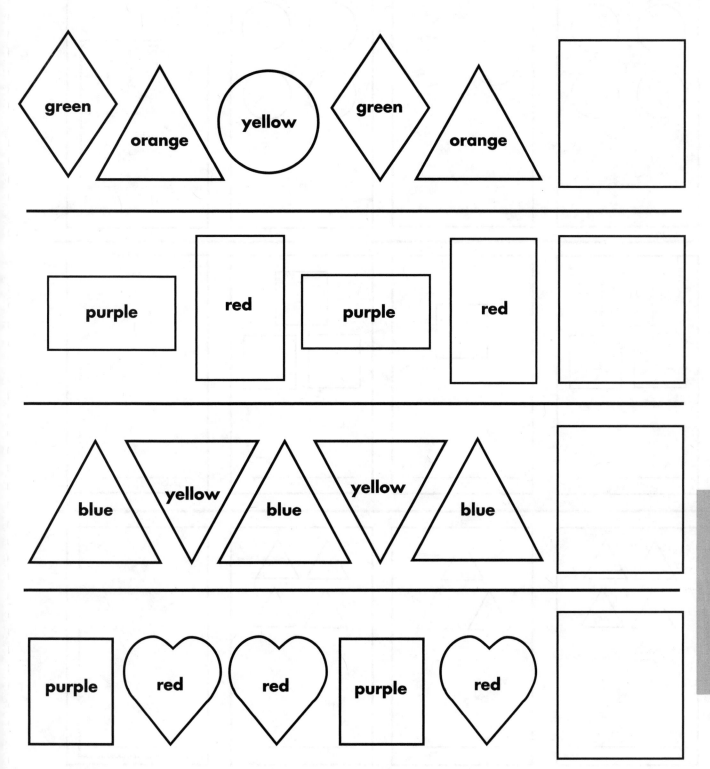

Patterns

In each row, ask the child to count the shapes in each box and write the number. Then discuss the pattern in the row to help the child decide how many of the shapes to draw in the empty box and which number to write.

Counting Patterns I

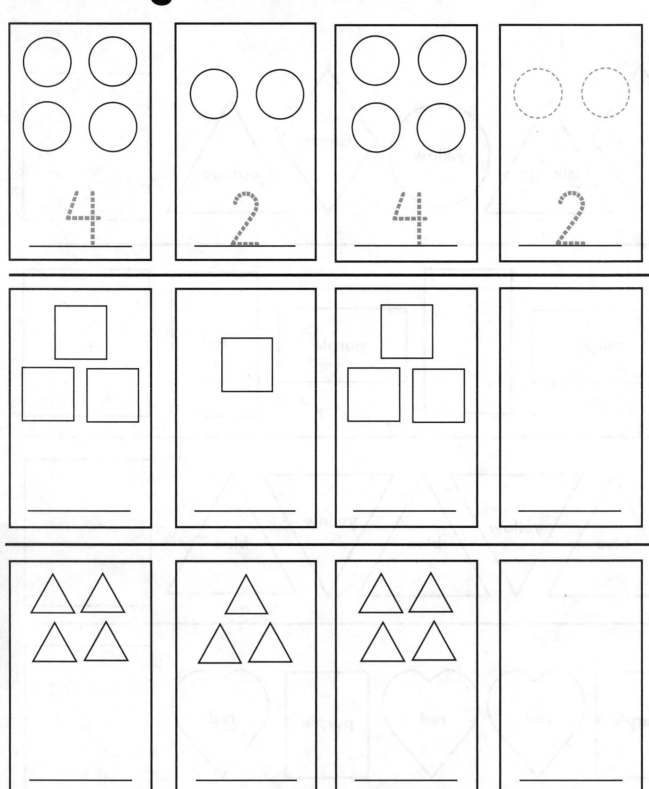

Counting; recognizing and continuing patterns (amounts)

In each row, ask the child to count the shapes in each box and write the number. Then discuss the pattern in the row to help the child decide how many of the shapes to draw in the empty box and which number to write.

Counting Patterns II

Ask the child to carefully look at the gray drum in the middle of the page and say aloud the pattern of shapes it shows in the center. Then ask the child to draw a line to every other drum whose center pattern matches that of the middle drum exactly.

Drum Patterns

Match.

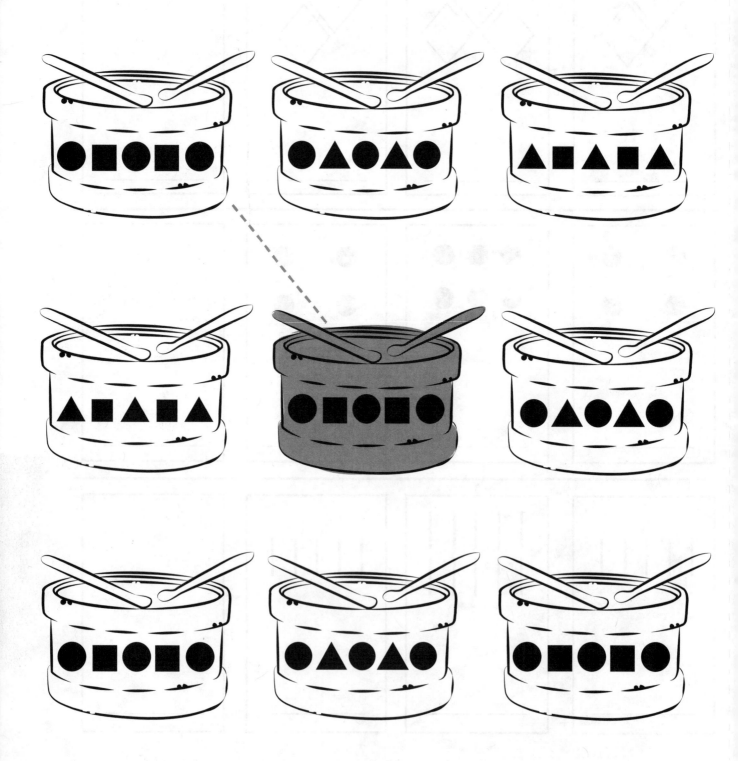

Recognizing and matching patterns

Ask the child to carefully look at the pattern on the gray wagon in the middle of the page and say aloud the pattern of shapes it shows. Then ask the child to draw a line to every other wagon whose center pattern matches that of the middle wagon exactly.

Wagon Patterns

Match.

Ask the child to write the number that continues the pattern in each row.

Number Patterns

3 2 3 2 3 --------

5 1 5 1 5 --------

1 4 1 4 1 --------

2 7 2 7 2 --------

Recognizing and continuing patterns; writing numbers

Ask the child to write the number that continues the pattern in each row.

More Number Patterns

 1 2 3 4 5

 6 7 8 9 10

2 1 4 2 1 _____

3 5 7 3 5 _____

6 2 9 6 2 _____

5 1 8 5 1 _____

Recognizing and continuing patterns; writing numbers

113

Ask the child to finish drawing the pattern inside the spaces to complete a path between the firefighter and his hose. Repeat the process for the carpenter and his hammer.

Path Finders 1

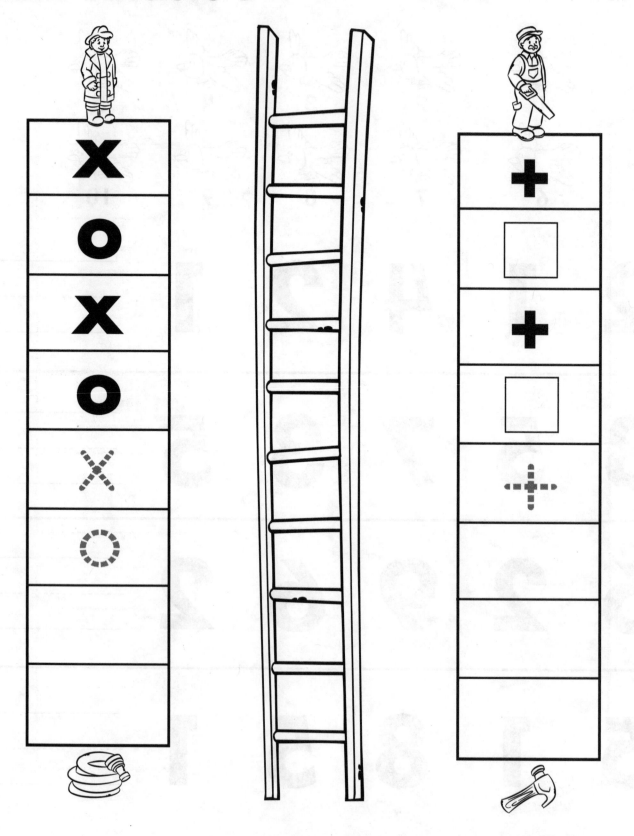

Recognizing and continuing patterns

Ask the child to finish drawing the pattern inside the spaces to complete a path between the teacher and her eraser and chalk. Repeat the process for the doctor and her stethoscope.

Path Finders II

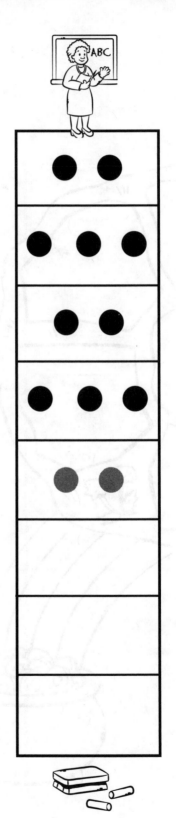

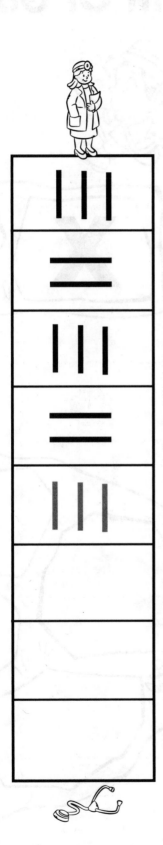

Recognizing and continuing patterns

115

Ask the child to identify the pattern in the path and then finish drawing it to reach the pot of gold.

Path Of Gold

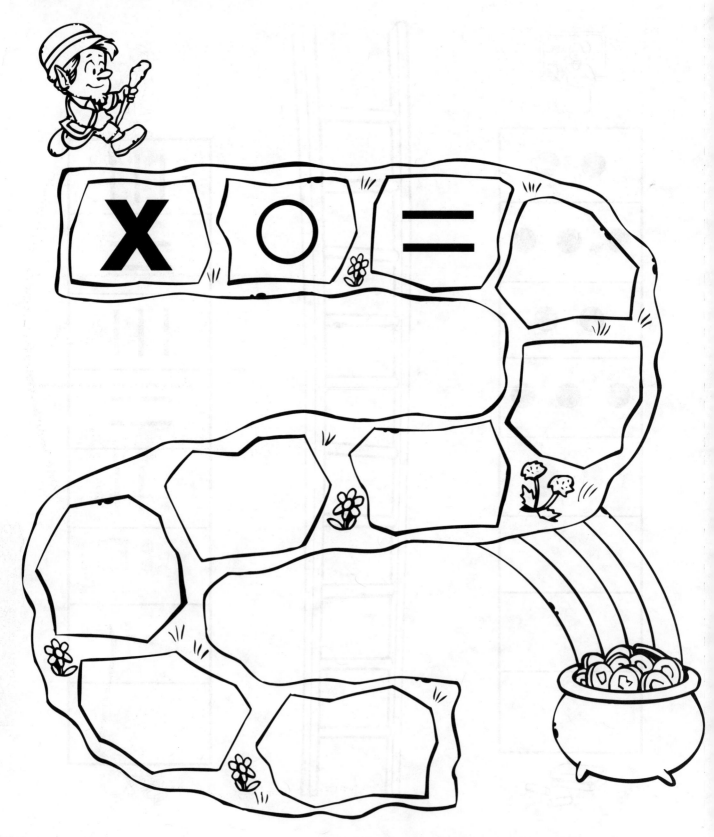

Recognizing and continuing patterns

Ask the child to use the color key to color the mitten.

Made-To-Order Mitten

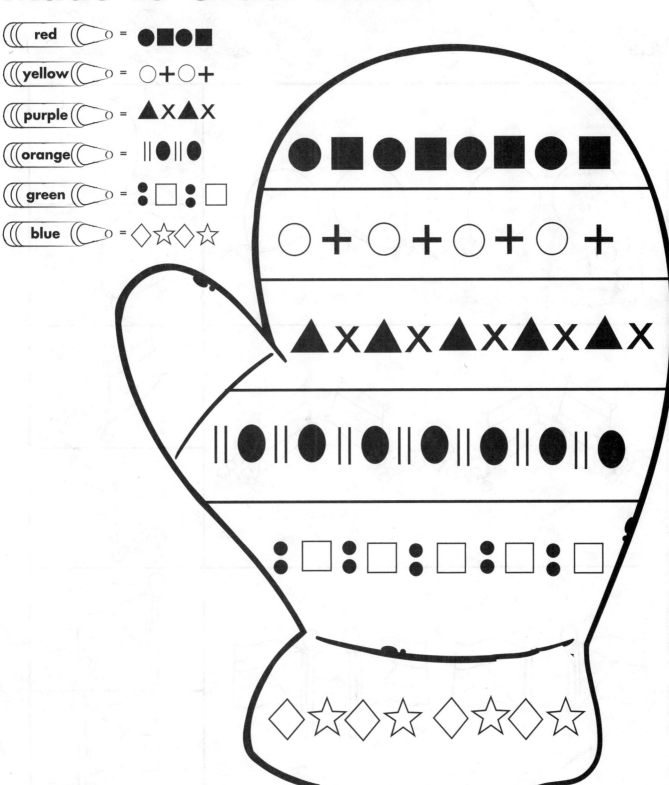

Ask the child to look at the pattern in each row. Point out that some of the objects are facing one way and some the other. Ask the child to circle the picture at the end of each row that completes the pattern.

The Way the Wind Blows

Circle.

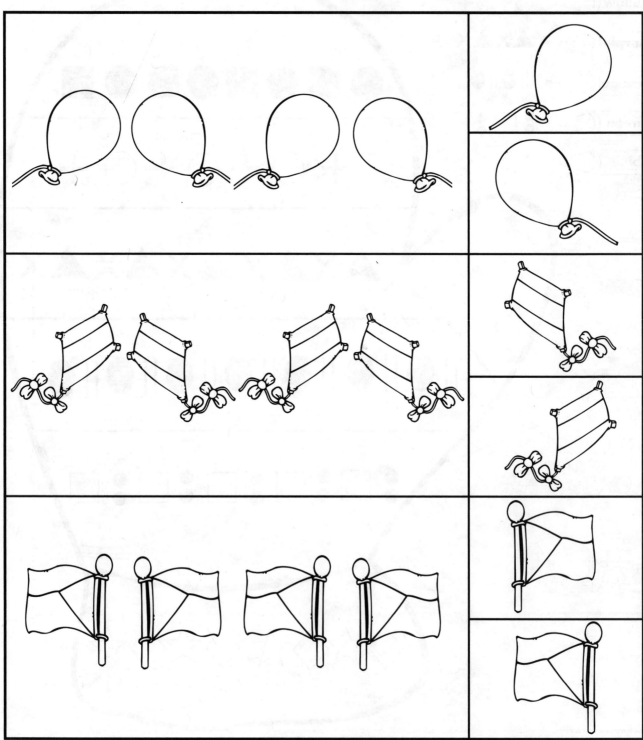

Recognizing and continuing patterns; directionality

Ask the child to look at the pattern in each column. Point out that some of the vehicles are facing one way and some the other. Ask the child to circle the vehicle at the end of each column that completes the pattern.

Which Way Wheels

Circle.

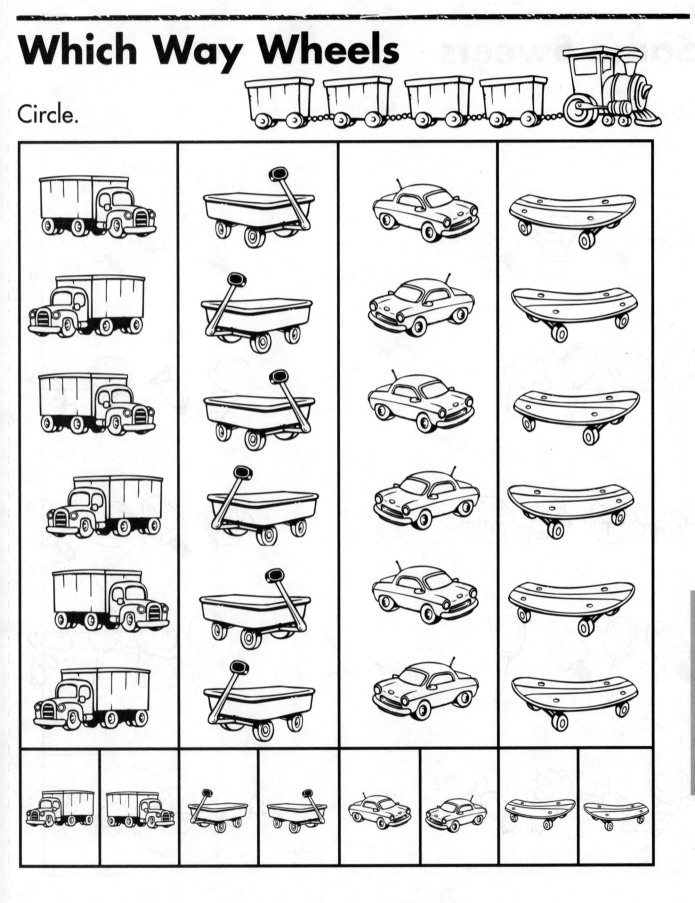

Ask the child to look at the pattern at the top of the left column, find its match in the right column and draw a line between the two. Continue for each pattern.

Same Sweets

Match.

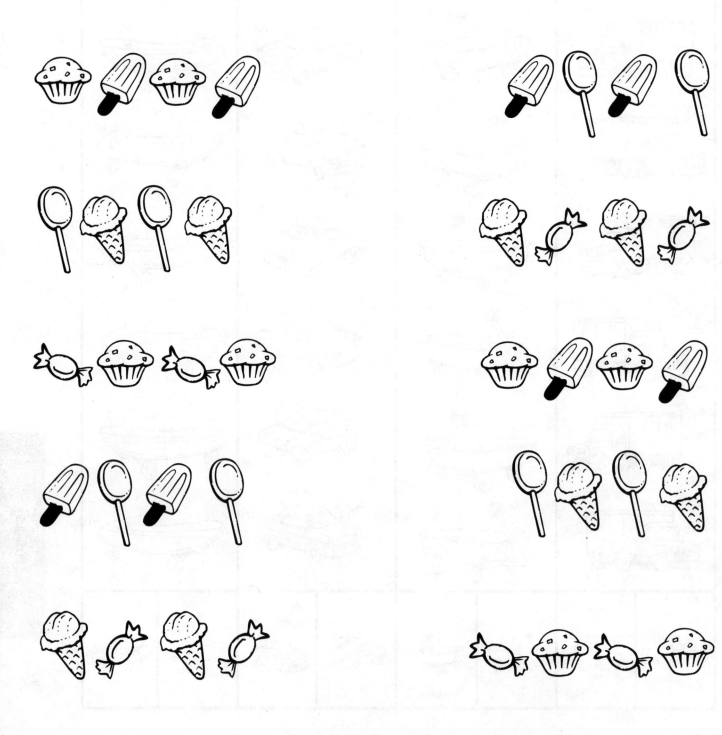

Recognizing and matching patterns

Ask the child to look at the pattern at the top of the left column, find its match in the right column and draw a line between the two. Continue for each pattern.

Bug Pals

Match.

Recognizing and matching patterns

121

Ask the child to look carefully at the pattern of letters shown on each of the caterpillars below. Help the child identify the two-letter pattern shown on each caterpillar. Then ask the child to write in the last two letters to complete the pattern.

Caterpil-letter!

Recognizing and continuing patterns; printing letters

Ask the child to look carefully at each row of letter patterns and say the pattern aloud. Then have him or her fill in the missing letters on the write-on lines provided.

Missing Letters

H P H P H P _____ P _____

T D T D T D _____ _____

K m K m K _____ _____ m

v _____ v S _____ S

S v _____ v S _____ S

Ask the child to color in the tulips according to the pattern/color key below.

Spring Flowers

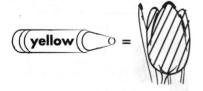 yellow = 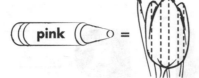 pink = 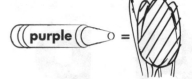 purple =

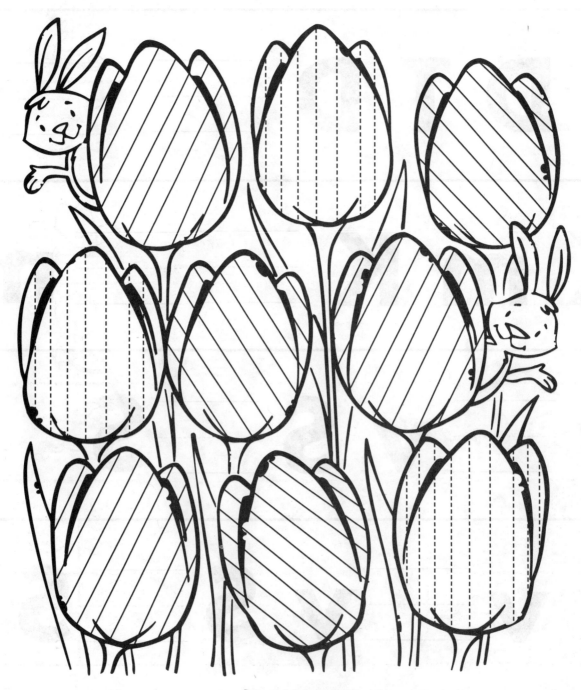

Recognizing patterns

Ask the child to look carefully at the patterns in the first column, then circle the two pictures that complete the pattern. Repeat for each column.

Pattern Rodeo

Patterns

Answer Key

As the child completes the pages in this section, review his or her answers. When you take the time to correct the work and explain mistakes, you're showing your child that you feel learning is important.

page 96

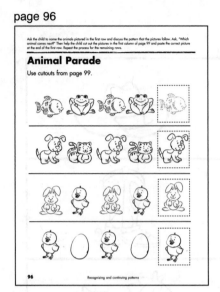

page 97

page 98

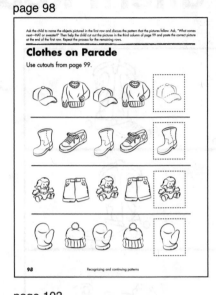

page 101

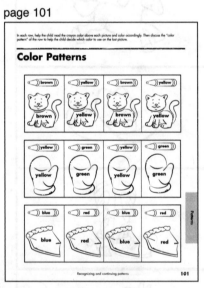

page 102

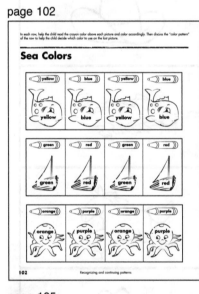

page 103

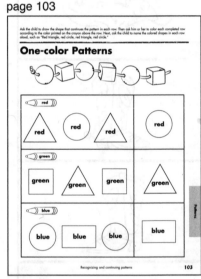

page 104

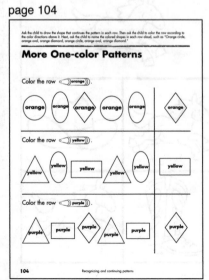

page 105

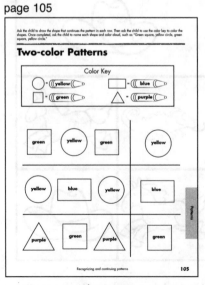

page 106

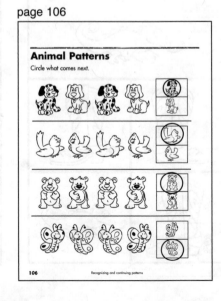

page 107

Ask the child to draw the shape that continues the pattern in each row. Then ask the child to color the shapes according to the color word printed on each of them and continue the color pattern for the shape he or she drew. Once completed, ask the child to name each colored shape aloud, such as "Green diamond, orange triangle, yellow circle, green diamond, orange triangle, yellow circle."

Colored Shape Patterns

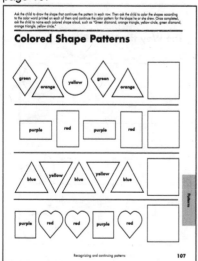

page 108

In each row, ask the child to count the shapes in each box and write the number. Then discuss the pattern in the row to help the child decide how many of the shapes to draw in the empty box and which number to write.

Counting Patterns I

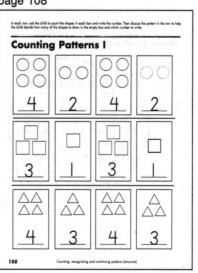

page 109

In each row, ask the child to count the shapes in each box and write the number. Then discuss the pattern in the row to help the child decide how many of the shapes to draw in the empty box and which number to write.

Counting Patterns II

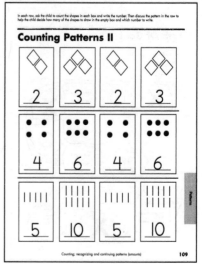

page 110

Ask the child to carefully look at the drum in the middle of the circle and say aloud the pattern of shapes it shows in the center. Then ask the child to draw a line to every other drum whose center pattern matches that of the middle drum exactly.

Drum Patterns
Match.

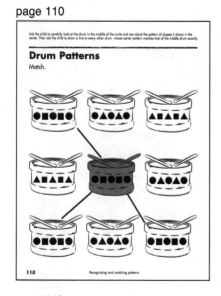

page 111

Ask the child to carefully look at the pattern on the wagon in the middle of the page and say aloud the pattern of shapes it shows. Then ask the child to draw a line to every other wagon whose center pattern matches that of the middle wagon exactly.

Wagon Patterns
Match.

page 112

Ask the child to write the number that continues the pattern in each row.

Number Patterns

page 113

Ask the child to write the number that continues the pattern in each row.

More Number Patterns

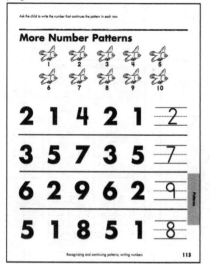

page 114

Ask the child to finish drawing the pattern inside the spaces to complete a path between the firefighter and his hose. Repeat the process for the carpenter and his hammer.

Path Finders I

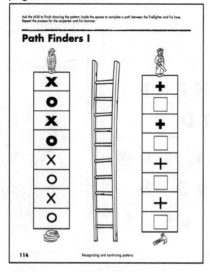

page 115

Ask the child to finish drawing the pattern inside the spaces to complete a path between the teacher and her eraser and chalk. Repeat the process for the doctor and her stethoscope.

Path Finders II

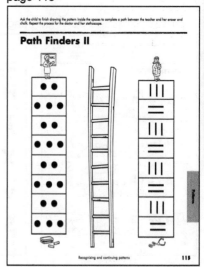

Patterns

Answers

127

page 116

Ask the child to identify the pattern in the path and then finish drawing it to reach the pot of gold.

Path Of Gold

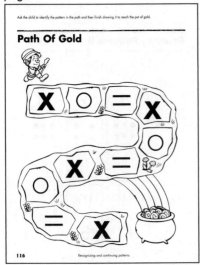

Recognizing and continuing patterns

page 117

Ask the child to use the color key to color the mitten.

Made-To-Order Mitten

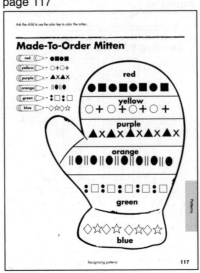

Recognizing patterns

page 118

Ask the child to look at the pattern in each row. Point out that some of the objects are facing one way and some the other. Ask the child to circle the picture at the end of each row that completes the pattern.

The Way the Wind Blows

Circle.

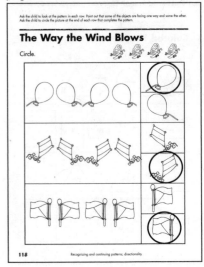

Recognizing and continuing patterns; directionality

page 119

Ask the child to look at the pattern in each column. Point out that some of the vehicles are facing one way and the other. Ask the child to circle the vehicle at the end of each column that completes the pattern.

Which Way Wheels

Circle.

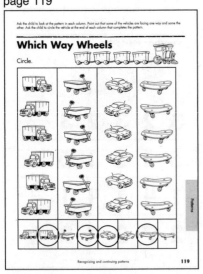

Recognizing and continuing patterns

page 120

Ask the child to look at the pattern at the top of the left column, find its match in the right column and draw a line between the two. Continue for each pattern.

Same Sweets

Match.

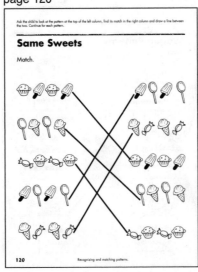

Recognizing and matching patterns

page 121

Ask the child to look at the pattern at the top of the left column, find its match in the right column and draw a line between the two. Continue for each pattern.

Bug Pals

Match.

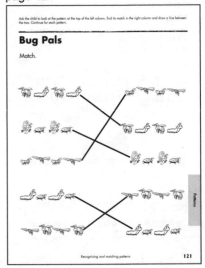

Recognizing and matching patterns

page 122

Ask the child to look carefully at the pattern of letters shown on each of the caterpillars below. Help the child identify the two-letter pattern shown on each caterpillar. Then ask the child to write in the last two letters to complete the pattern.

Caterpil-letter!

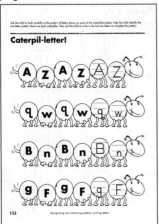

Recognizing and continuing patterns; printing letters

page 123

Ask the child to look carefully at each row of letter patterns and say the pattern aloud. Then have him or her fill in the missing letters on the write-on lines provided.

Missing Letters

HPHP⊞P⊞
TDTD⊤⊡
KmK⊞K m
vＳvＳ⊻Ｓ
ＳvＳvＳ⊻Ｓ

Recognizing and continuing patterns; printing letters

page 124

Ask the child to color the tulips according to the pattern/color key below.

Spring Flowers

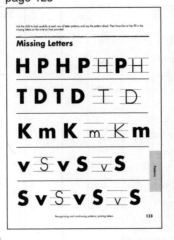

Recognizing patterns

page 125

Ask the child to look carefully at the patterns in the first column, then circle the two pictures that complete the pattern. Repeat for each pattern.

Pattern Rodeo

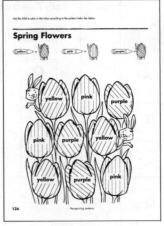

Recognizing and continuing patterns

Answers

Point to each "coin" at the top of the page and read its value aloud to the child. Point out the different sizes of the "coins." Next, ask the child to point to each "coin" and read the number that tells its value— the amount of cents it represents. Below, ask the child to color the "coins" according to the color key.

Loose Change

Color Key

orange = 1¢   green = 10¢

blue = 5¢   red = 25¢

How Many Cents?

The mark used to show cent or cents is ¢.

Color the (1¢)s you need in order to buy each treat.

Money awareness: recognizing the cents symbol: ¢

Read aloud the sentences at the top of the page to the child.

Money & Time

5¢ or More

Color the toys that cost one .

 8¢

 5¢

5¢

 9¢

7¢

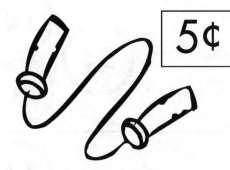 5¢

5¢

How many s would you need to buy all the 5¢ toys? _____

Ask the child to color the hat in the first row and then read how many cents it costs. Point to the coins shown on the right side of the row and ask the child to color in those needed to purchase the hat. Repeat this process for the remaining rows.

Hat Sale!

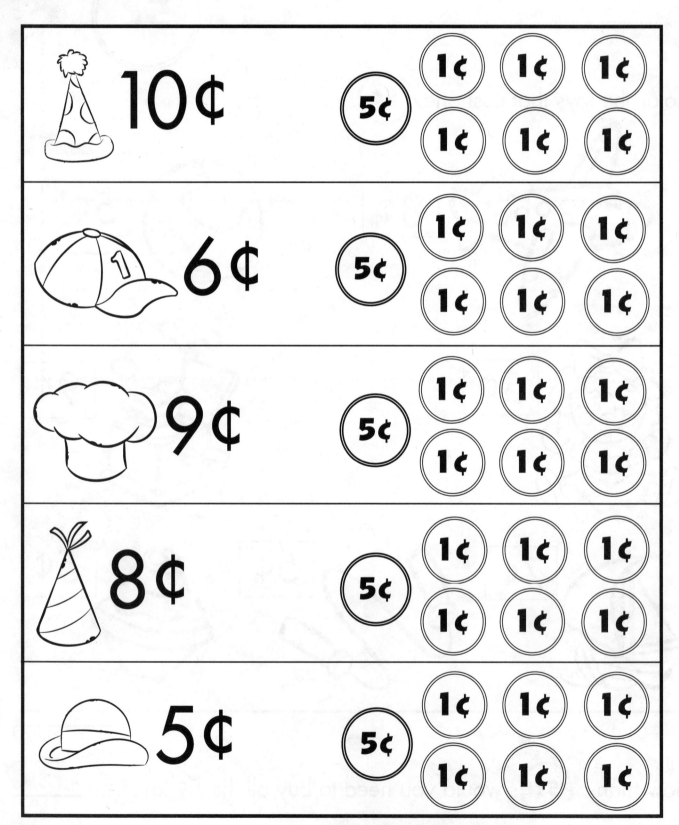

Understanding money value

Read aloud the sentences below and ask the child to write the answers on the write-on lines provided.

Making Cents!

How many (1¢)s make 5¢?	How many (5¢)s make 5¢?
How many (5¢)s make 10¢?	How many (1¢)s make 10¢?

Match.

10¢

5¢

7¢

What Costs 10¢?

10¢

Color the fruit that costs one .

10¢   8¢   5¢   10¢

9¢   10¢   10¢

_____

- - - - - - - - -

How many **10¢**s would you need to buy all the 10¢ fruits?_____

Understanding money value

Mouse Money Match

Match. Color.

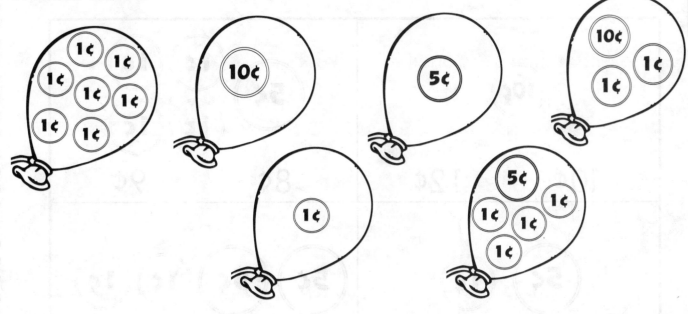

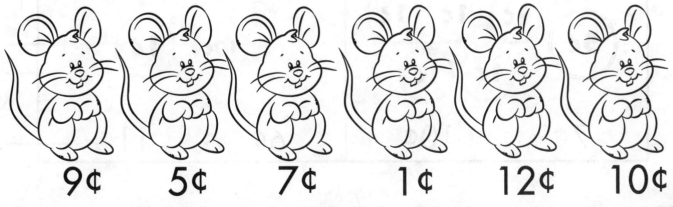

9¢   5¢   7¢   1¢   12¢   10¢

Ask the child to circle the correct amount in each box.

It All Adds Up

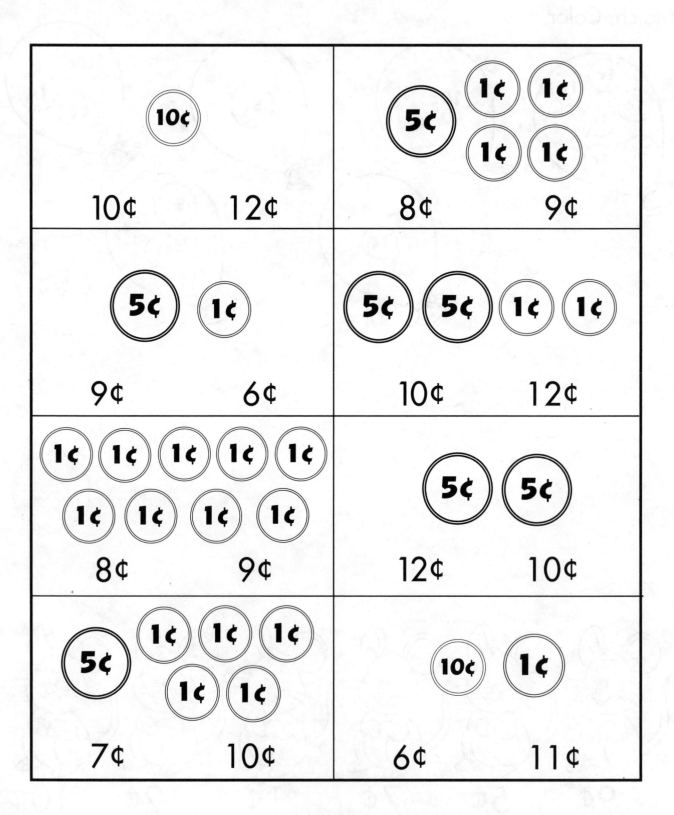

10¢　　12¢	8¢　　9¢
9¢　　6¢	10¢　　12¢
8¢　　9¢	12¢　　10¢
7¢　　10¢	6¢　　11¢

Understanding money value

Read aloud the sentence at the top of the page to the child.

Money & Time

What is 25¢?

Color the s blue.

Put an **X** on what is not a .

5¢   1¢   25¢   10¢   25¢

25¢   1¢   5¢   1¢   10¢   5¢

25¢   10¢   25¢   5¢   10¢

Help the child to understand the color key below and then ask him or her to color the picture accordingly. When the picture is completed, ask the child to tell what the picture shows.

Ocean Treasure

green = 5¢   orange = 10¢
blue = 6¢   yellow = 25¢

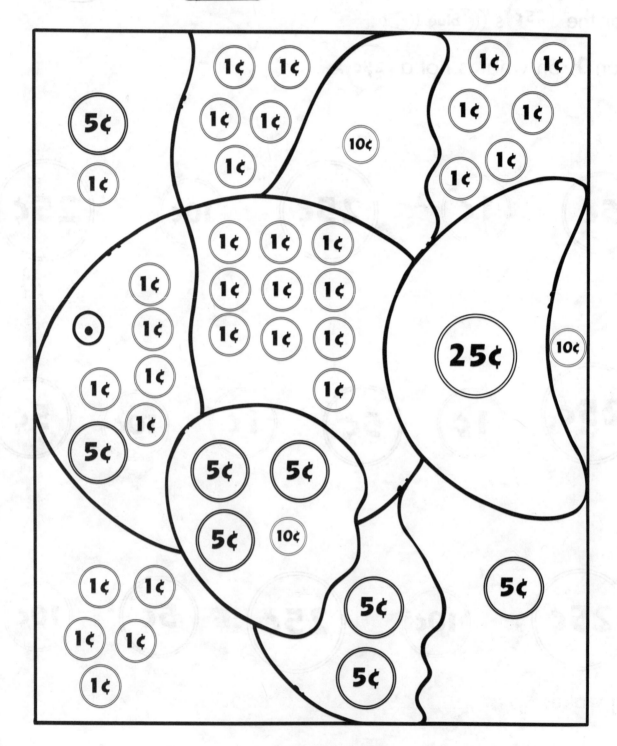

Understanding money value

Ask the child to use a pencil to trace the clock outline, the numerals, the larger arrow pointing to the number 12, and the shorter arrow pointing to the number 6. Say, "The arrows make the minute and hour hands for this clock. The minute hand is big, the hour hand is little. The minute hand is on the 12. The hour hand is pointing to the 6. This clock shows six o'clock." Have the child write in the numeral to complete the sentence below.

Frog Wakes Up At Six O'Clock!

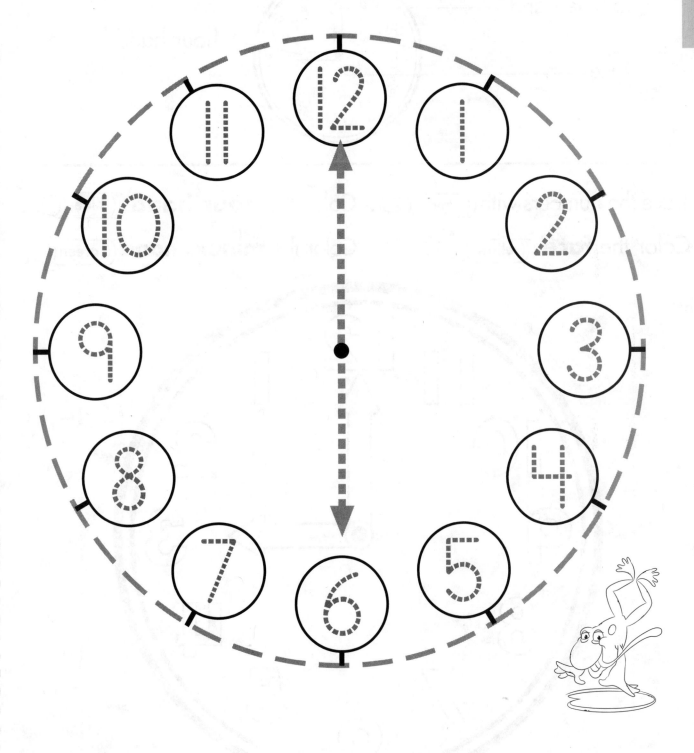

Frog wakes up at _____ o'clock.

Telling time

139

Read or help the child to read aloud the labels on the parts of the clock shown at the top of the page. Explain that the clock front is called the *face*. Remind the child that the little hand is called the *hour hand* and that the big hand is called the *minute hand*. Then have the child color the clock at the bottom of the page according to the color key instructions.

Tick-Tock Parts

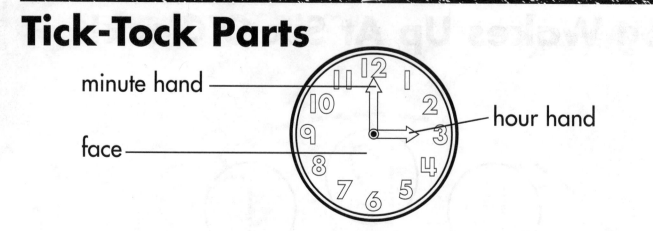

minute hand

hour hand

face

Trace the numbers with (((red (((⟩ . Color the **hour hand** (((blue (((⟩ .

Color the **face** (((yellow (((⟩ . Color the **minute hand** (((green (((⟩ .

Understanding parts of a clock

Explain to the child that when the big hand is on the 12, the little hand always points to an hour. Look at the row of clocks and read the times shown aloud to the child. Stress the word *o'clock*. Then have the child look at the clocks below and circle the correct time.

All About O'Clock

  1 o'clock   2 o'clock 3 o'clock   4 o'clock   5 o'clock   6 o'clock

| 1 o'clock | 2 o'clock | 3 o'clock | 4 o'clock | 5 o'clock | 6 o'clock |

| 7 o'clock | 8 o'clock | 9 o'clock | 10 o'clock | 11 o'clock | 12 o'clock |

2 o'clock   11 o'clock

10 o'clock   4 o'clock

3 o'clock   6 o'clock

8 o'clock   4 o'clock

Telling time

141

More O'Clocks

1 o'clock   3 o'clock

9 o'clock   3 o'clock

3 o'clock   5 o'clock

12 o'clock   7 o'clock

9 o'clock   5 o'clock

12 o'clock   4 o'clock

Explain that the clock hands spin all the way around the clock two full times for each complete day and night and that we use the words "in the morning," "in the afternoon," and "at night" to describe different times of day. Ask the child to tell you what time it is on the first clock on the left, and then ask him or her to draw a picture in the box on the right that shows what he or she is usually doing at that time of the morning.

What I Do in the Morning

Morning Time

What I Do

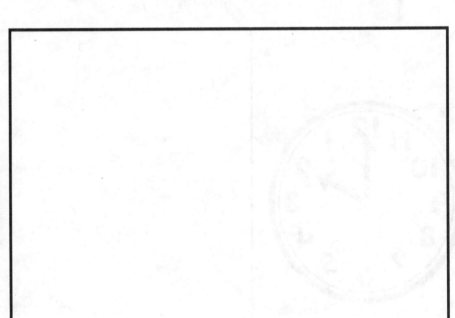

Refer to the directions on page 143.

What I Do in the Afternoon

Afternoon Time

What I Do

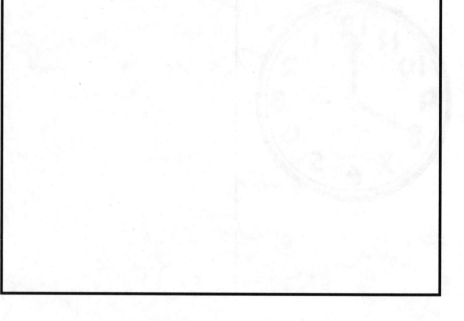

Telling time

What I Do at Night

Night Time

What I Do

Explain that both the clocks below show the same time and that we can write the time with the term, *o'clock* or we can write it another way. Point out the use of the colon and two zeros as another way to write *o'clock*. Explain that the numeral to the left of the colon shows the hour and that the numerals to the right show the minutes.

I Can Write Time

3 o'clock

3:00

_____ :00

_____ :00

_____ :00

_____ :00

Telling time; writing time

Bzzzzy Writing Time

Write the time.

_____ :00

_____ :00

_____ :00

_____ :00

Ask the child to trace the hour hands on the first two clocks to show the time indicated. Then ask him or her to draw in the hour hands on the five clocks below. Remind the child that the hour hand is shorter than the minute hand.

What Hour Is It?

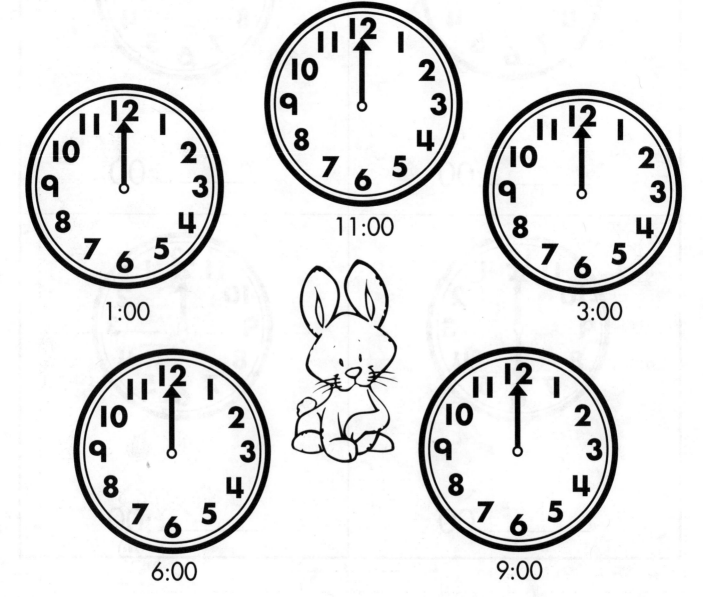

2:00

8:00

11:00

1:00

3:00

6:00

9:00

Telling time; drawing in the hour hand

Answer Key

As the child completes the pages in this section, review his or her answers. When you take the time to correct the work and explain mistakes, you're showing your child that you feel learning is important.

page 129

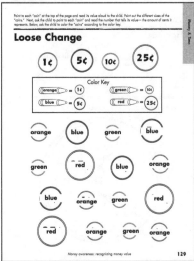

page 130

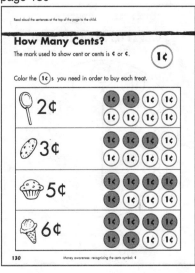

page 131

page 132

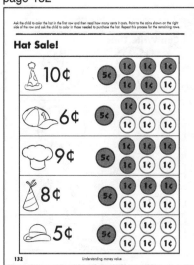

page 133

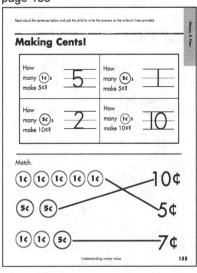

page 134

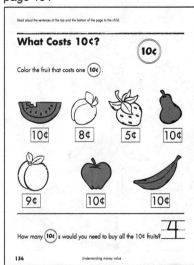

page 135

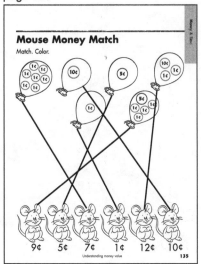

page 136

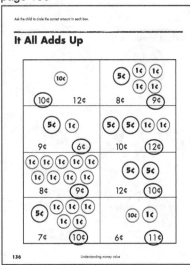

page 137

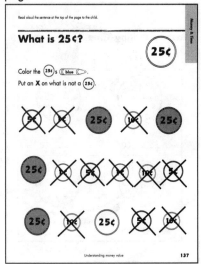

Answers

149

page 138

Help the child to understand the color key below and then ask him or her to color the picture accordingly. When the picture is completed, ask the child to tell what the picture shows.

Ocean Treasure

- green = 5¢
- blue = 6¢
- orange = 10¢
- yellow = 25¢

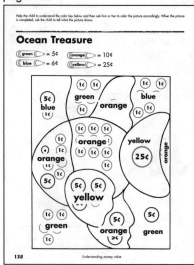

138 — Understanding money value

page 139

Ask the child to use a pencil to trace the clock outline, the numerals, the larger arrow pointing to the number 12, and the shorter arrow pointing to the number 6. Say, "The arrows make the minute and hour hands for this clock. The minute hand is big, the hour hand is little. The minute hand is on the 12. The hour hand is pointing to the 6. This clock shows six o'clock." Have the child write in the numeral to complete the sentence below.

Frog Wakes Up At Six O'Clock!

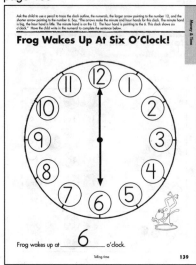

Frog wakes up at ___6___ o'clock.

139 — Telling time

page 140

Read or help the child to read aloud the labels on the parts of the clock shown at the top of the page. Explain that the clock front is called the face. Remind the child that the little hand is called the hour hand and that the big hand is called the minute hand. Then have the child color the clock at the bottom of the page according to the color key instructions.

Tick-Tock Parts

minute hand

face — hour hand

Trace the numbers with red .   Color the hour hand blue .
Color the face yellow .   Color the minute hand green .

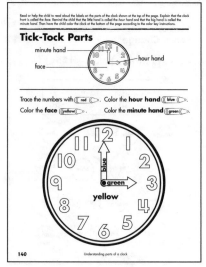

140 — Understanding parts of a clock

page 141

Explain to the child that when the big hand is on the 12, the little hand always points to an hour. Look at the row of clocks and read the times shown aloud to the child. Stress the word o'clock. Then have the child look at the clocks below and circle the correct time.

All About O'Clock

1 o'clock 2 o'clock 3 o'clock 4 o'clock 5 o'clock 6 o'clock
7 o'clock 8 o'clock 9 o'clock 10 o'clock 11 o'clock 12 o'clock

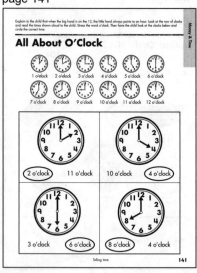

(2 o'clock) 11 o'clock   10 o'clock (4 o'clock)

3 o'clock (6 o'clock)   (8 o'clock) 4 o'clock

Telling time 141

page 142

Ask the child to look at the clocks and circle the correct time. NOTE: When the child reaches the last clock (bottom right), point out that with both hands on the 12, the big minute hand can "hide" the little hour hand.

More O'Clocks

1 o'clock (3 o'clock)   9 o'clock (3 o'clock)

3 o'clock (5 o'clock)   12 o'clock (7 o'clock)

(9 o'clock) 5 o'clock   (12 o'clock) 4 o'clock

142 Telling time

page 146

Explain that both the clocks below show the same time and that we can write the time with the term, o'clock, or we can write it another way. Point out the use of the colon and two zeros as another way to write o'clock. Explain that the numeral to the left of the colon shows the hour and that the numerals to the right show the minutes.

I Can Write Time

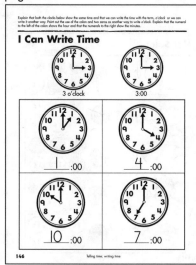

3 o'clock   3:00

___1___ :00   ___4___ :00

___10___ :00   ___7___ :00

146 — Telling time; writing time

page 147

Bzzzzy Writing Time

Write the time.

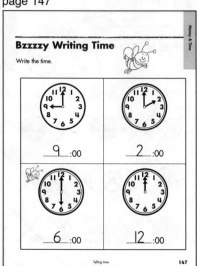

___9___ :00   ___2___ :00

___6___ :00   ___12___ :00

Telling time 147

page 148

Ask the child to trace the hour hands on the first two clocks to show the time indicated. Then ask him or her to draw in the hour hands on the five clocks below. Remind the child that the hour hand is shorter than the minute hand.

What Hour Is It?

2:00   8:00

11:00

1:00   3:00

6:00   9:00

148 — Telling time; drawing in the hour hand

Ask the child to circle all the letters **Aa** in the title below. Then ask him or her to name the objects shown in the picture and circle those that have the same beginning sound as **apple**. At the bottom of the page, ask the child to trace and then write the letters.

Aa/Astronaut Ann's apple

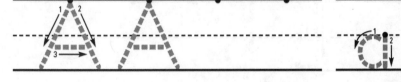

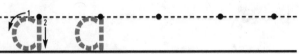

Tracing and printing letters; recognizing letter sounds

Ask the child to circle all the letters **Bb** in the title below. Then ask him or her to name the objects shown inside the balloons and color the balloons whose objects begin with **B**. At the bottom of the page, ask the child to trace and then write the letters.

Bb/Balloons for Baby Bear

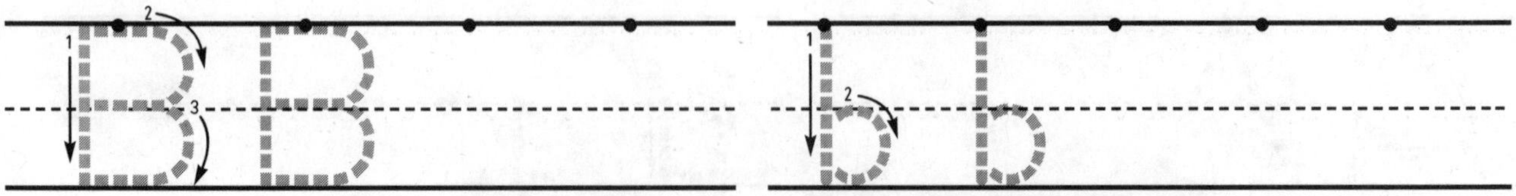

Tracing and printing letters; recognizing letter sounds

Ask the child to circle all the letters **Cc** in the title below. Then ask him or her to name the pictures shown in boxes on the side of the camel and color the picture in each box that begins with **C**. At the bottom of the page, ask the child to trace and then write the letters.

Cc/A cap for Carl Camel

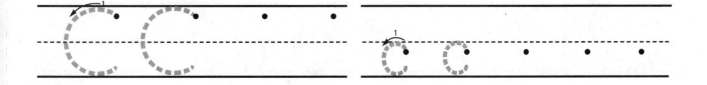

Ask the child to circle all the letters **Dd** in the title below. Then ask him or her to help the dog get to the doghouse by following the pictures that begin with **D**. At the bottom of the page, ask the child to trace and then write the letters.

Dd/Dinosaur Daniel's dish

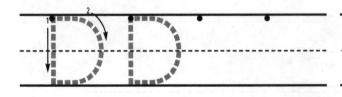 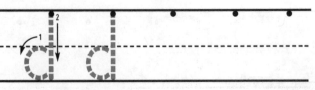

Tracing and printing letters; recognizing letter sounds

Ask the child to circle all the letters **Ee** in the title below. Then ask him or her to look at the pictures shown on the elephant, and circle the picture in each box that has the same beginning sound as **elephant**. At the bottom of the page, ask the child to trace and then write the letters.

Ee/Elephant's egg

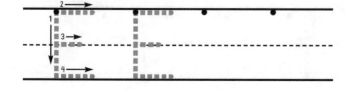

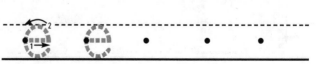

Tracing and printing letters; recognizing letter sounds

155

Ask the child to circle all the letters **Ff** in the title below. Then ask him or her to look at the pictures below, and color the spaces with pictures that begin with **F**. At the bottom of the page, have the child trace and then write the letters.

Ff/Frank's funny faucet

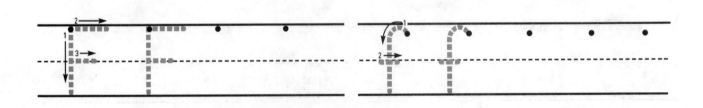

Tracing and printing letters; recognizing letter sounds

Ask the child to circle all the letters **Gg** in the title below. Then ask him or her look at the pictures below and draw a line from each picture to the letter it begins with. At the bottom of the page, have the child trace and then write the letters.

Gg/Goose on a garden gate

Gg   Bb   Aa   Ff   Cc   Gg

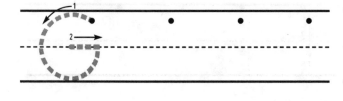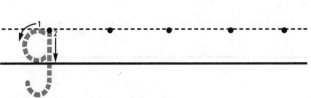

Ask the child to circle all the letters **Hh** in the title below. Then ask him or her to look at the pictures below and draw a line from the **Hh** in the box to each picture that begins with an **H**. At the bottom of the page, ask the child to trace and then write the letters.

Hh/Harry Hippo's horn

Tracing and printing letters; recognizing letter sounds

Ask the child to circle all the letters **Ii** in the title below. Then ask him or her to look at the scene below and color each ice block that contains a picture that begins with **I**. At the bottom of the page, ask the child to trace and then write the letters.

Ii/Inchworm's igloo

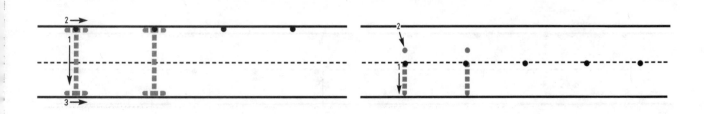

Ask the child to circle all the letters **Jj** in the title below. Then ask him or her to look at the pictures in the ends of the jacks and cross out the pictures that do not begin with the letter **J**. At the bottom of the page, ask the child to trace and then write the letters.

Jj/A jar for Jimmy's jacks

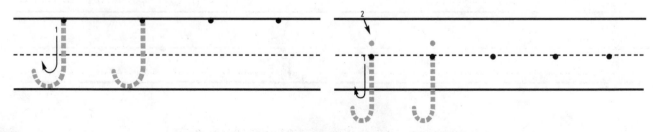

Tracing and printing letters; recognizing letter sounds

[1] Ask the child to circle all the letters **Kk** in the title below. [2] Ask the child to connect the circular dots from **A** to **K**.
[3] Ask the child to connect the square dots from **a** to **k**. [4] Ask him or her to circle the pictures in the kites that start
with the letter **K**. [5] At the bottom of the page, ask the child to trace and then write the letters.

Kk/Kangaroo's kites

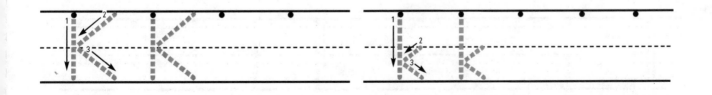

Tracing and printing letters; recognizing letter sounds

161

Ask the child to circle all the letters **Ll** in the title below. Then ask him or her to look at the scene below and circle each object that begins with **L**. At the bottom of the page, ask the child to trace and then write the letters.

Ll/Lynn Lion's living room

Ll

Tracing and printing letters; recognizing letter sounds

Ask the child to circle all the letters **Mm** in the title below. Then ask him or her to find the path to the cheese by following the pictures that begin with **M**. At the bottom of the page, ask the child to trace and then write the letters.

Mm/Mouse's warm mittens

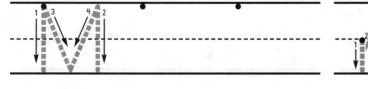

Ask the child to circle all the letters **Nn** in the title below. Then ask him or her to draw a line from the nurse to all the objects on the carts that begin with the letter **N**. At the bottom of the page, ask the child to trace and then write the letters.

Nn/A needle for Nurse Nancy

Tracing and printing letters; recognizing letter sounds

Ask the child to circle all the letters **Oo** in the title below. Then ask him or her to look at each picture card the octopus is holding and circle the letter that stands for the picture's beginning sound. At the bottom of the page, ask the child to trace and then write the letters.

Oo/Octopus loves olives

O   H

L   J

N   I

M   O

N   K

L   O

O   M

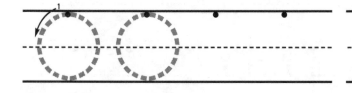

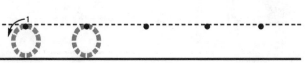

Ask the child to circle all the letters **Pp** in the title below. Then ask him or her to draw a line from **Pp** to each picture that begins with **P**. At the bottom of the page, ask the child to trace and then write the letters.

Pp/A puppet for Patty Pig

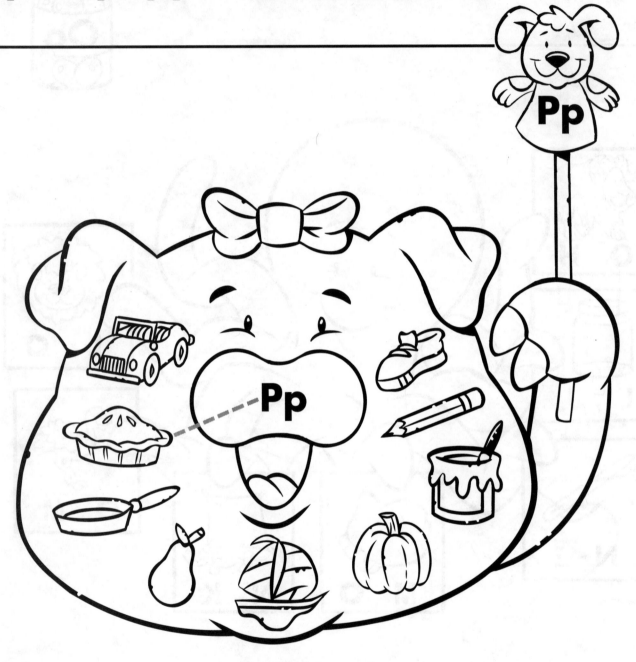

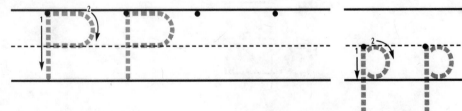

Tracing and printing letters; recognizing letter sounds

Ask the child to circle all the letters **Qq** in the title below and all the pictures on the quilt that begin with **Q**. Then ask him or her to connect the dots from **A** to **Q** and color the whole quilt. At the bottom of the page, ask the child to trace and then write the letters.

Qq/The Queen's quilt

[1] Ask the child to circle all the letters **Rr** in the title below. [2] Then ask him or her to use a red crayon to color the robot and to circle all the pictures in the rocket that begin with **R**. At the bottom of the page, ask the child to trace and then write the letters.

Rr/Rick Robot's rocket

Tracing and printing letters; recognizing letter sounds

Ask the child to circle all the letters **Ss** in the title below. Then ask him or her to circle all pictures around the seal that begin with **S**. At the bottom of the page, ask the child to trace and then write the letters.

Ss/Seal plays in the sun

Ask the child to circle all the letters **Tt** in the title below. Then ask him or her to circle all the pictures on the turtle's shell that begin with **T**. At the bottom of the page, ask the child to trace and then write the letters.

Tt/Turtle talks on the telephone

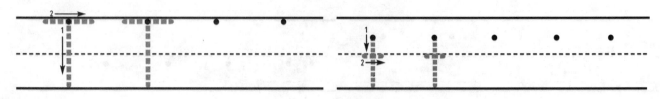

Tracing and printing letters; recognizing letter sounds

Ask the child to circle all the letters **Uu** in the title below. Then ask him or her color the picture according to the color key. At the bottom of the page, ask the child to trace and then write the letters.

Uu/An umbrella for Umpire

Color Key

Color **R** green   Color **S** blue

Color **T** brown   Color **U** yellow

Uu

Ask the child to circle all the letters **Vv** in the title below. Then ask him or her to circle all the pictures in the large valentine that begin with **V**. At the bottom of the page, ask the child to trace and then write the letters.

Vv/Very nice valentine

Tracing and printing letters; recognizing letter sounds

Ask the child to circle all the letters **Ww** in the title below. Then ask him or her to draw a line from the spider in its web to all the pictures around it that begin with **W**. At the bottom of the page, ask the child to trace and then write the letters.

Ww/Worm watches the web

Tracing and printing letters; recognizing letter sounds

173

Ask the child to circle all the letters **Xx** in the title below. Then ask him or her to draw lines to connect each body part in the top row with its corresponding x-ray in the bottom row. At the bottom of the page, ask the child to trace and then write the letters.

Xx/Extra x-rays of Max

Xx

  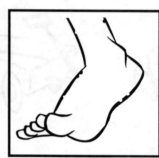 

 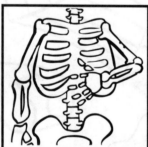  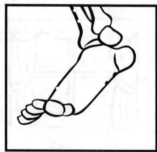

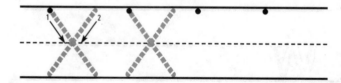 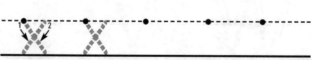

Tracing and printing letters; recognizing letter sounds

Ask the child to circle all the letters **Yy** in the title below. Then ask him or her to circle all the pictures on the yak that begin with **Y**. At the bottom of the page, ask the child to trace and then write the letters.

Yy/Yak's in Lynn's yard

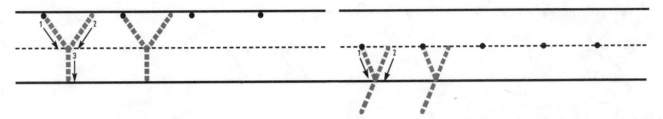

Tracing and printing letters; recognizing letter sounds

175

Ask the child to circle all the letters **Zz** in the title below. Then ask him or her to draw a connecting line from Aa to **Zz** in alphabetic order to help the zebra find a path to the **zoo**. At the bottom of the page, ask the child to trace and then write the letters.

Zz/Zebra finds the zoo

Zz

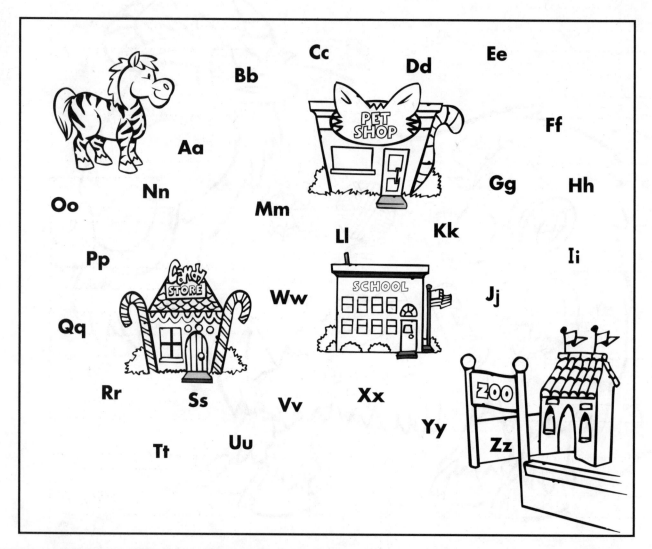

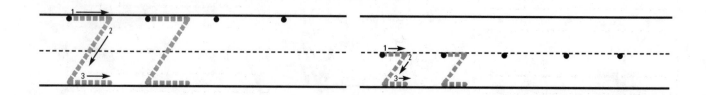

Tracing and printing letters; recognizing letter sounds

Look-Alikes

Match.

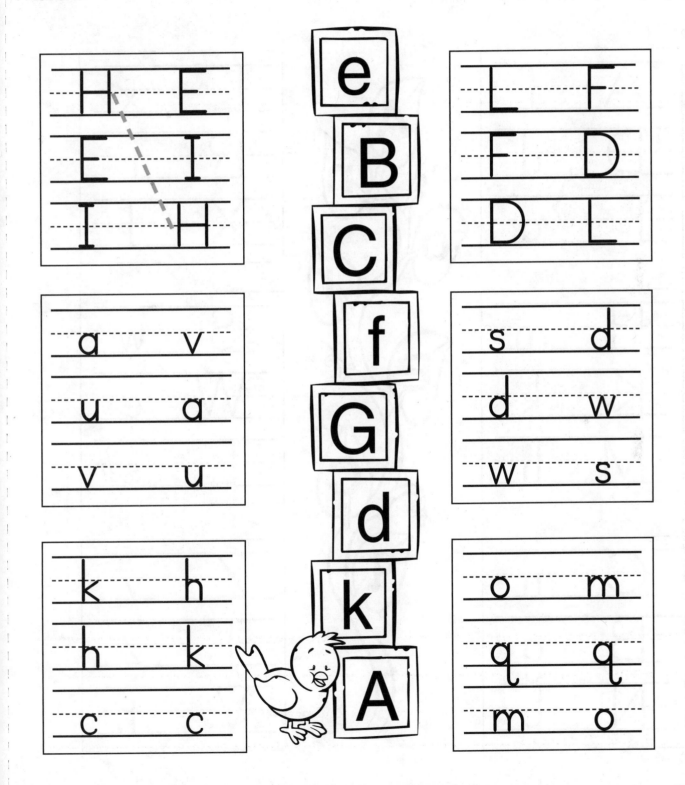

Partners

Match.

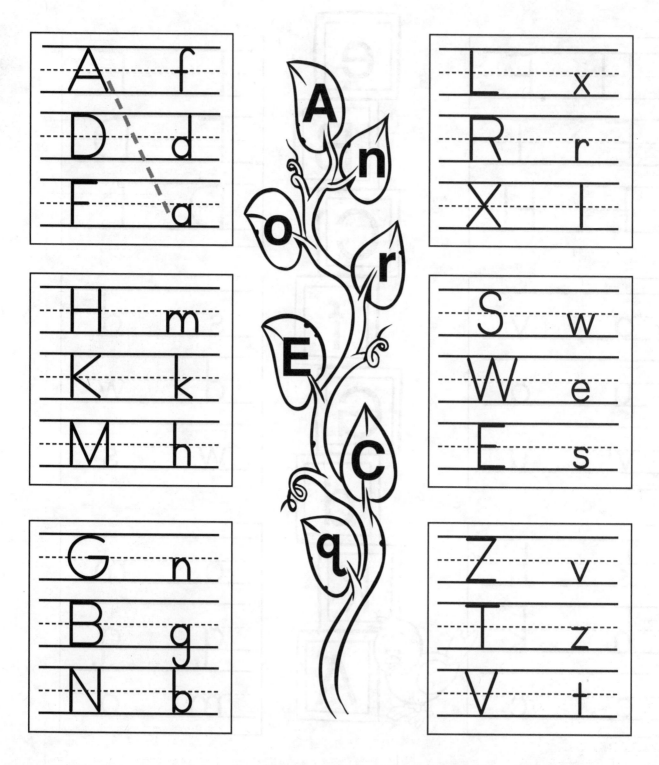

Matching uppercase and lowercase forms of letters

Answer Key

As the child completes the pages in this section, review his or her answers. When you take the time to correct the work and explain mistakes, you're showing your child that you feel learning is important.

page 151

page 152

page 153

page 154

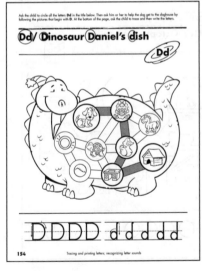

page 155

page 156

page 157

page 158

page 159

page 160

Ask the child to circle all the letters Jj in the title below. Then ask him or her to look at the pictures in the ends of the jacks and cross out the pictures that do not begin with the letter J. At the bottom of the page, ask the child to trace and then write the letters.

Jj / A jar for Jimmy's jacks

J J J j j j j j j j

160   Tracing and printing letters; recognizing letter sounds

page 161

[1] Ask the child to circle all the letters Kk in the title below. [2] Ask the child to connect the circular dots from A to K. [3] Ask the child to connect the square dots from a to k. [4] Ask him or her to circle the pictures in the kites that start with the letter K. [5] At the bottom of the page, ask the child to trace and then write the letters.

Kk / Kangaroo's Kites

K K K K k k k k k

Tracing and printing letters; recognizing letter sounds   161

page 162

Ask the child to circle all the letters Ll in the title below. Then ask him or her to look at the scene below and circle each object that begins with L. At the bottom of the page, ask the child to trace and then write the letters.

Ll / Lynn Lion's living room

L L L L l l l l l

162   Tracing and printing letters; recognizing letter sounds

page 163

Ask the child to circle all the letters Mm in the title below. Then ask him or her to find the path to the cheese by following the pictures that begin with M. At the bottom of the page, ask the child to trace and then write the letters.

Mm / Mouse's warm mittens

M M M m m m m m

Tracing and printing letters; recognizing letter sounds   163

page 164

Ask the child to circle all the letters Nn in the title below. Then ask him or her to draw a line from the nurse to all the objects on the carts that begin with the letter N. At the bottom of the page, ask the child to trace and then write the letters.

Nn / A needle for Nurse Nancy

N N N N n n n n n

164   Tracing and printing letters; recognizing letter sounds

page 165

Ask the child to circle all the letters Oo in the title below. Then ask him or her to look at each picture card the octopus is holding and circle the letter that stands for the picture's beginning sound. At the bottom of the page, ask the child to trace and then write the letters.

Oo / Octopus loves olives

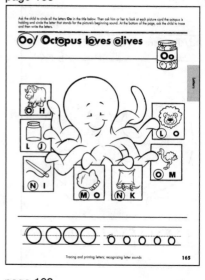

O O O O o o o o o

Tracing and printing letters; recognizing letter sounds   165

page 166

Ask the child to circle all the letters Pp in the title below. Then ask him or her to draw a line from Pp to each picture that begins with P. At the bottom of the page, ask the child to trace and then write the letters.

Pp / A puppet for Patty Pig

P P P P p p p p p

166   Tracing and printing letters; recognizing letter sounds

page 167

Ask the child to circle all the letters Qq in the title below and all the pictures on the quilt that begin with Q. Then ask him or her to connect the dots from A to Q and color the whole quilt. At the bottom of the page, ask the child to trace and then write the letters.

Qq / The Queen's quilt

Q Q Q Q q q q q q

Tracing and printing letters; recognizing letter sounds   167

page 168

[1] Ask the child to circle all the letters Rr in the title below. [2] Then ask him or her to use a red crayon to color the robot and to circle all the robot to the pictures in the rocket that begin with R. At the bottom of the page, ask the child to trace and then write the letters.

Rr / Rick Robot's rocket

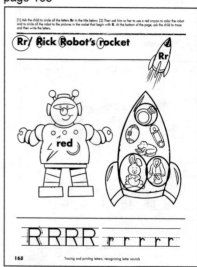

R R R R r r r r r

168   Tracing and printing letters; recognizing letter sounds

page 169

Ask the child to circle all the letters **Ss** in the title below. Then ask him or her to circle all the pictures around the seal that begin with **S**. At the bottom of the page, ask the child to trace and then write the letters.

Ss/ Seal plays in the sun

Ss

S S S S   s s s s s

Tracing and printing letters; recognizing letter sounds   169

page 170

Ask the child to circle all the letters **Tt** in the title below. Then ask him or her to circle all the pictures on the turtle's shell that begin with **T**. At the bottom of the page, ask the child to trace and then write the letters.

Tt/ Turtle talks on the telephone

Tt

170   Tracing and printing letters; recognizing letter sounds

page 171

Ask the child to circle all the letters **Uu** in the title below. Then ask him or her color the picture according to the color key. At the bottom of the page, ask the child to trace and then write the letters.

Uu/ An umbrella for Umpire

Color Key
Color R green   Color S blue
Color T brown   Color U yellow

Uu

U U U U   u u u u u

Tracing and printing letters; recognizing letter sounds   171

page 172

Ask the child to circle all the letters **Vv** in the title below. Then ask him or her to circle all the pictures in the large valentine that begin with **V**. At the bottom of the page, ask the child to trace and then write the letters.

Vv/ Very nice valentine

Vv

V V V V   v v v v v

172   Tracing and printing letters; recognizing letter sounds

page 173

Ask the child to circle all the letters **Ww** in the title below. Then ask him or her to draw a line from the spider in its web to all the pictures around it that begin with **W**. At the bottom of the page, ask the child to trace and then write the letters.

Ww/ Worm watches the web

Ww

W W W   w w w w w

Tracing and printing letters; recognizing letter sounds   173

page 174

Ask the child to circle all the letters **Xx** in the title below. Then ask him or her to draw a lines that connect each body part in the top row with its corresponding x-ray in the bottom row. At the bottom of the page, ask the child to trace and then write the letters.

Xx/ Extra x-rays of Max

Xx

X X X X   x x x x x

174   Tracing and printing letters; recognizing letter sounds

page 175

Ask the child to circle all the letters **Yy** in the title below. Then ask him or her to circle all the pictures on the yak that begin with **Y**. At the bottom of the page, ask the child to trace and then write the letters.

Yy/ Yak's in Lynn's yard

Yy

Y Y Y Y   y y y y y

Tracing and printing letters; recognizing letter sounds   175

page 176

Ask the child to circle all the letters **Zz** in the title below. Then ask him or her to draw a connecting line from Aa to Zz in alphabetic order to help the zebra find a path to the **zoo**. At the bottom of the page, ask the child to trace and then write the letters.

Zz/ Zebra finds the zoo

Zz

Z Z Z Z   z z z z z

176   Tracing and printing letters; recognizing letter sounds

page 177

Look-Alikes

Match.

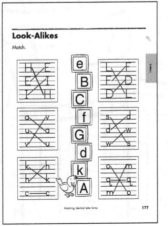

Matching identical letter forms   177

page 178

Partners

Match.

178   Matching uppercase and lowercase forms of letters

What's Going Up?

Connect the dots from **a** to **o**. Color the picture.

Developing fine motor control; following alphabetical order

Ask the child to draw a line through the maze to help the farmer find his way home. Then ask him or her to color the picture.

Autumn Leaves

Developing fine motor control

183

Ask the child to color the picture according to the color key below. Then help the child recognize the picture of the sea star under the water.

At the Beach

Color Key

yellow = **A**   orange = **B**   blue = **C**

Guess what — it's a sea star!

Developing visual discrimination

Ask the child to color the picture according to the color key below. Then help the child recognize the picture of the sea horse under the water.

What Is It?

Color Key

Color the shapes with ●s ((green)) .
Color the other shapes ((brown)) .

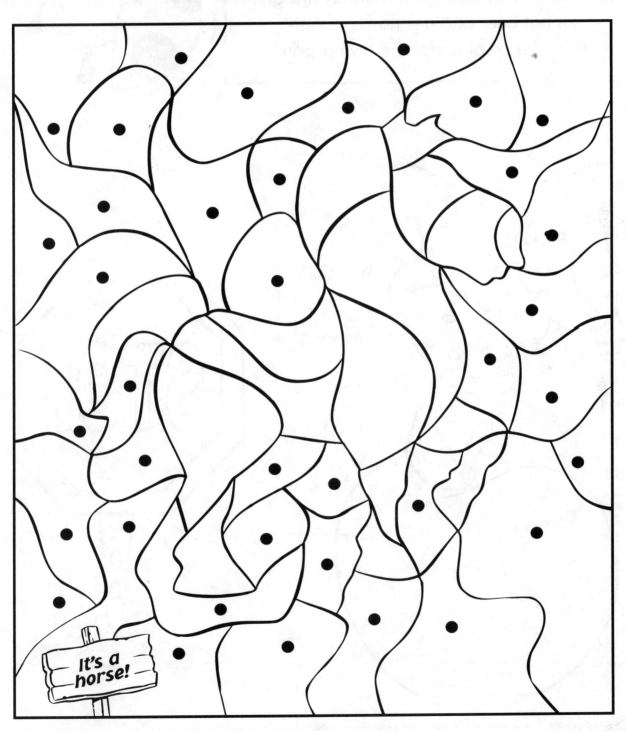

It's a horse!

Developing visual discrimination

Read the rhyme aloud. Point to the picture of the ladybug and say, "Ladybugs are red." Ask the child to color the ladybug's shell red and then ask him or her to identify each item pictured at the bottom of the page and color it red.

Red

Ladybug
Ladybug, Ladybug, fly away home!
Your house is on fire, your children are gone.
All but one, and her name is Ann,
And she crept under the frying pan.

Understanding colors; recognizing color names

Read the rhyme aloud. Point to the sun and say, "The sun is yellow." Ask the child color the sun yellow and then ask him or her to identify each item pictured at the bottom of the page and color it yellow.

Yellow

Sally Go Round the Sun
Sally go round the sun,
Sally go round the moon,
Sally go round the chimney-pots
On a Sunday afternoon.

Understanding colors; recognizing color names

187

Ask the child to find the letters **P I N K** in the picture and circle them. Explain that the letters may be shaped a little differently than usual. Say, "P-I-N-K spells pink." Point out the flamingos and say "Flamingos have pink feathers." Then ask the child to color the picture.

Pink and Pretty

Recognizing color names; developing visual discrimination

Ask the child to find the letters **P I G** in the picture and circle them. Explain that the letters may be shaped a little differently than usual. Say, "P-I-G spells pig." Then ask the child to color the picture.

What a Pig!

Developing visual discrimination

189

Blue

Little Boy Blue
Little Boy Blue, come blow your horn;
The sheep's in the meadow,
the cow's in the corn.
Where is the boy who looks after the sheep?
He's under the haystack, fast asleep.

Ask the child to find and circle the letters **F O X** in the picture. Say, "F-O-X spells fox." Ask the child to point out the fox in the picture and then to color the picture.

Sly Fox

Developing visual discrimination

191

Hiding in the Jungle

Circle the s. Color the picture.

Developing visual discrimination

Read the rhyme aloud. Point to the pickles and say, "Pickles are green." Ask the child to color the pickles green and then to identify each item pictured at the bottom of the page and color it green.

Green

Peter Piper
Peter Piper picked a peck of pickled peppers;
A peck of pickled peppers Peter Piper picked.
If Peter Piper picked a peck of pickled peppers,
Where's the peck of pickled peppers
Peter Piper picked?

Understanding colors; recognizing color names

193

Orange

Peter, Peter, Pumpkin Eater
Peter, Peter, pumpkin eater,
Had a wife and couldn't keep her;
He put her in a pumpkin shell
And there he kept her very well.

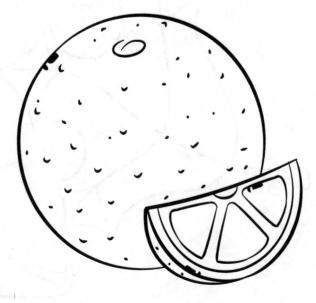

Understanding colors; recognizing color names

Dairy Delights

Circle the , the 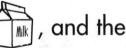, and the ⟁. Color the picture.

Ask the child to color the picture according to the color key. Then ask him or her what is on the leaf.

Yellow Fellow

yellow = **1**   black = **2**   green = **3**

Look! It's a caterpillar!

Developing visual discrimination

Purple

Little Jack Horner
Little Jack Horner sat in a corner,
Eating a Christmas pie;
He put in his thumb, and pulled out a plum,
And said, "What a good boy am I!"

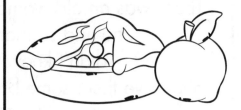

Getting Ready to Read I

Understanding colors; recognizing color names

Brown

Old Woman in a Shoe
There was an old woman who lived in a shoe.
She had so many children she
didn't know what to do.
She gave them some broth without any bread,
And sang to them sweetly, and sent them to bed.

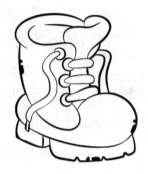

HONEY

Understanding colors; recognizing color names

Ask the child to color the chick according to the color key.

Chicken Little

It's a
baby chick!

Developing visual discrimination

199

Help the child to understand the directions on how to color the shapes with the dot. Then ask the child what animal is revealed in the picture. Finally, ask the child to color the duck as he or she wishes.

Lucky Ducks

Color the shapes with a ● blue.

Quack, quack! A duck!

Developing visual discrimination

Read the rhyme aloud. Ask the child to identify each item pictured at the bottom of the page and then color it black.

Black

Baa, Baa, Black Sheep
Baa, Baa, black sheep, have you any wool?
Yes, sir, yes, sir, three bags full;
One for my master and one for my dame,
And one for the little boy who lives down the lane.

Understanding colors; recognizing color names

What's Alike?

Match.

Classifying objects

Ask the child to find the letters **F L O A T** in the picture and circle them. Say, "F-L-O-A-T spells float. Otters like to float in the water." Ask the child to color the picture.

Safe in the Seaweed

Developing visual discrimination

Under the Sun

Circle the s. Color the picture.

Developing visual discrimination

Clothing Go-Togethers

Match.

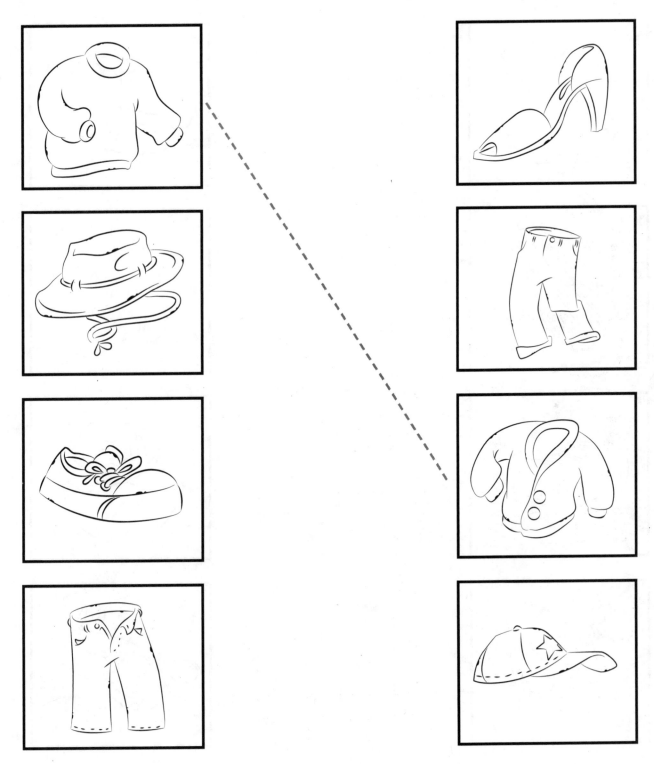

Ask the child to point to and name each item in the left hand column. Then ask him or her to identify the fruit, the nut, the bread and the vegetable. Say, "Draw a line to connect each of the items that go together."

Food Go-Togethers

Match.

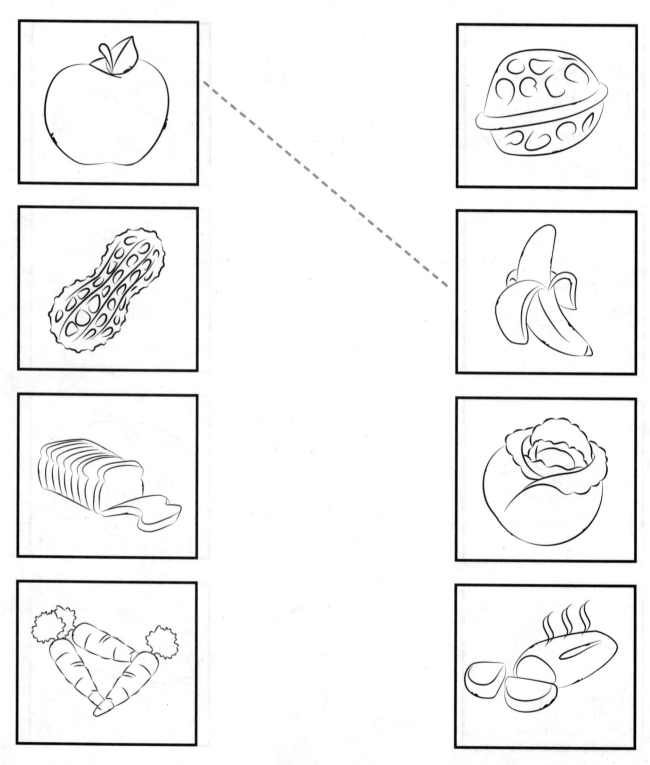

Classifying objects

We Belong Together

Match.

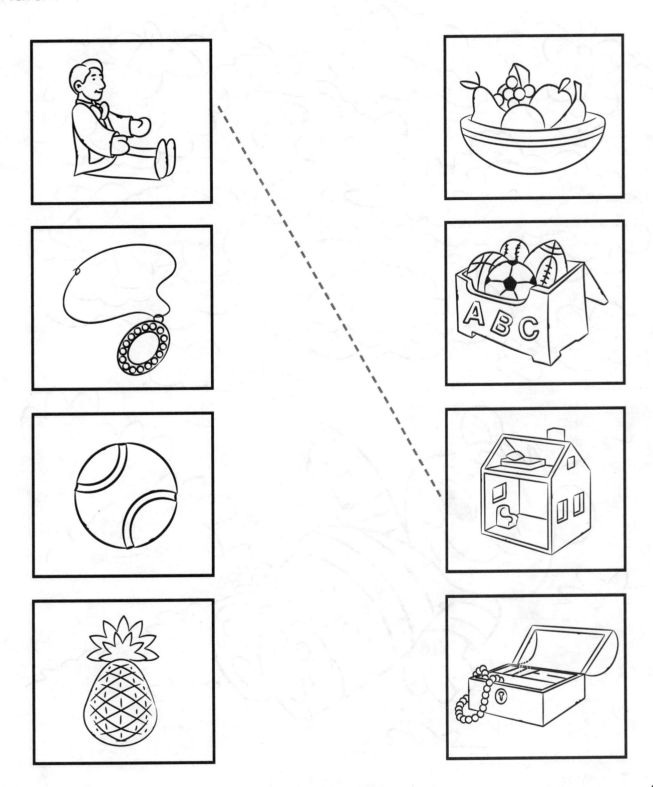

Ask the child to find the animals hidden in the clouds and circle them. Then ask him or her to color the picture.

Cloud Critters

Developing visual discrimination

Hats Off

Match.

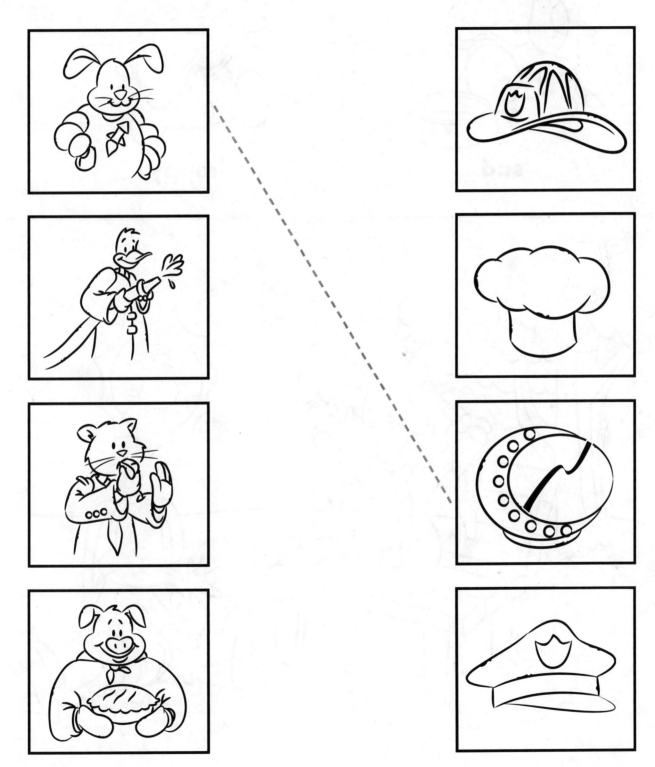

Classifying objects

209

Point to the dog that is sad and ask, "Why is it sad?" Repeat for the happy dog. Explain that the words *sad* and *happy* are called opposites. Ask the child to find the sad rabbit and color it blue, then to find the happy rabbit and color it yellow. Ask why one rabbit is sad and the other is happy. Then ask the child to color the rest of the picture.

Why Happy?

sad

happy

　　　　　Understanding opposites

Ask the child whether the largest clown is happy or sad. Then ask, "What's the opposite of happy?" and invite the child to color the small clown that shows the opposite of happy. Repeat for the tennis players. Point out the words *happy* and *sad* next to the smaller pictures.

Why Sad?

happy

sad

happy

sad

Understanding opposites

Ask the child to point to the lion that's out of his cage and then to the lion that's in his cage. Point to the words *in* and *out*. Explain that they are called opposites. Then say, "Find the dog that is in the doghouse and color it blue. Color the dog that's out brown."

In and Out

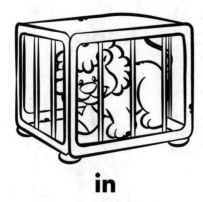

in

out

Understanding opposites

Discuss whether the largest dog is in or out of the bed. Ask, "What is the opposite of in?" Ask the child to color the small dog that shows the opposite. Repeat for the bears. Point out the words *in* and *out* next to the smaller pictures.

More In and Out

in

out

in

out

Understanding opposites

213

Answer Key

As the child completes the pages in this section, review his or her answers. When you take the time to correct the work and explain mistakes, you're showing your child that you feel learning is important.

page 182

page 183

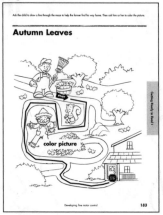

page 184

page 185

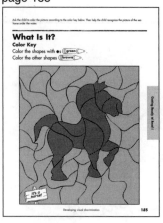

page 186

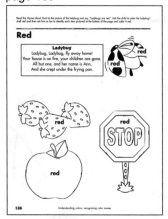

page 187

page 188

page 189

page 190

page 191

Ask the child to find and color the letters F O X in the picture. Say, "F-O-X spells fox." Ask the child to point out the fox in the picture and then to color the picture.

Sly Fox

color picture

Developing visual discrimination 191

page 192

Hiding in the Jungle

Circle the 🚙s. Color the picture.

color picture

192 Developing visual discrimination

page 193

Read the rhyme aloud. Point to the pickles and say, "Pickles are green." Ask the child to color the pickles green and then to identify each item pictured at the bottom of the page and color it green.

Green

Peter Piper
Peter Piper picked a peck of pickled peppers;
A peck of pickled peppers Peter Piper picked.
If Peter Piper picked a peck of pickled peppers,
Where's the peck of pickled peppers
Peter Piper picked?

green

green

green

green

Understanding colors; recognizing color names 193

page 194

Read the rhyme aloud. Point to the pumpkin and say, "A pumpkin is orange." Ask the child to color the pumpkin, and then identify each item pictured at the bottom of the page and color it orange.

Orange

Peter, Peter, Pumpkin Eater
Peter, Peter, pumpkin eater,
Had a wife and couldn't keep her;
He put her in a pumpkin shell
And there he kept her very well.

orange

orange

orange

orange

194 Understanding colors; recognizing color names

page 195

Dairy Delights

Circle the 🥛 the, 🥛 and the 🧀. Color the picture.

color picture

Developing visual discrimination 195

page 196

Ask the child to color the picture according to the color key. Then ask him or her what is on the leaf.

Yellow Fellow

yellow = 1   black = 2   green = 3

Look! It's a caterpillar!

196 Developing visual discrimination

page 197

Read the rhyme aloud. Point to the plum and say, "A plum is purple." Ask the child to identify each item pictured at the bottom of the page and color it purple.

Purple

Little Jack Horner
Little Jack Horner sat in a corner,
Eating a Christmas pie;
He put in his thumb, and pulled out a plum,
And said, "What a good boy am I!"

purple

purple

purple

Understanding colors; recognizing color names 197

page 198

Read the rhyme aloud. Ask the child to color the high-topped shoe brown. Then ask him or her to identify each item pictured at the bottom of the page and color it brown.

Brown

Old Woman in a Shoe
There was an old woman who lived in a shoe.
She had so many children she
didn't know what to do.
She gave them some broth without any bread,
And sang to them sweetly, and sent them to bed.

brown

brown

brown

brown

198 Understanding colors; recognizing color names

page 199

Ask the child to color the chick according to the color key.

Chicken Little

yellow = ◯   orange = △ ▢ ⬭

It's a baby chick!

Developing visual discrimination 199

page 200

Help the child to understand the directions on how to color the shapes with the dot. Then ask the child what animal is revealed in the picture. Finally, ask the child to color the duck as he or she wishes.

Lucky Ducks

Color the shapes with a ● blue.

Quack, quack! A duck!

200 Developing visual discrimination

page 201

Read the rhyme aloud. Ask the child to identify each item pictured at the bottom of the page and then color it black.

Black

Baa, Baa, Black Sheep
Baa, Baa, black sheep, have you any wool?
Yes, sir, yes, sir, three bags full;
One for my master and one for my dame,
And one for the little boy who lives down the lane.

black

black

black

Understanding colors; recognizing color names 201

page 202

What's Alike

Match.

202 Classifying objects

Ask the child to find the letters **F L O A T** in the picture and circle them. Say, "F-L-O-A-T spells float. Otters like to float in the water." Ask the child to color the picture.

Safe in the Seaweed

color picture

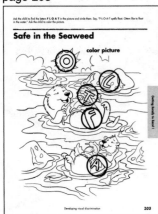

Developing visual discrimination   203

Under the Sun

Circle the 🐛 s. Color the picture.

color picture

204   Developing visual discrimination

Clothing Go-Togethers

Match.

Classifying objects   205

Ask the child to point to and name each item in the left-hand column. Then ask him or her to identify the fruit, the nut, the bread and the vegetable. Say, "Draw a line to connect each of the items that go together."

Food Go-Togethers

Match.

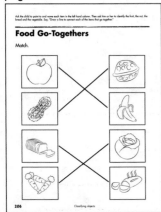

206   Classifying objects

We Belong Together

Match.

Classifying objects   207

Ask the child to find the animals hidden in the clouds and circle them. Then ask him or her to color the picture.

Cloud Critters

color picture

208   Developing visual discrimination

Hats Off

Match.

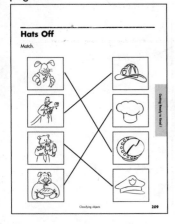

Classifying objects   209

Point to the dog that is sad and ask, "Why is it sad?" Repeat for the happy dog. Explain that the words sad and happy are called opposites. Ask the child to find the sad rabbit and color it blue, then to find the happy rabbit and color it yellow. Ask why one rabbit is sad and the other is happy. Then ask the child to color the rest of the picture.

Why Happy?

sad   happy

color picture

yellow

blue

210   Understanding opposites

Ask the child whether the largest clown is happy or sad. Then ask, "What's the opposite of happy?" and invite the child to color the small clown that shows the opposite of happy. Repeat for the tennis players. Point out the words happy and sad next to the smaller pictures.

Why Sad?

happy

sad

happy

sad

Understanding opposites   211

Ask the child to point to the lion that's out of his cage and then to the lion that's in his cage. Point to the words in and out. Explain that they are called opposites. Then say, "Find the dog that is in the doghouse and color it blue. Color the dog that's out brown."

In and Out

in   out

blue

brown

212   Understanding opposites

Discuss whether the largest dog is in or out of the bed. Ask, "What is the opposite of in?" Ask the child to color the small dog that shows the opposite. Repeat for the bears. Point out the words in and out next to the smaller pictures.

More In and Out

in

out

in

out

Understanding opposites   213

216   Answers

After the child has filled in the blanks in the activity below, ask him or her to use the picture clues to figure out each completed word.

A Is for Apple

Trace and write.

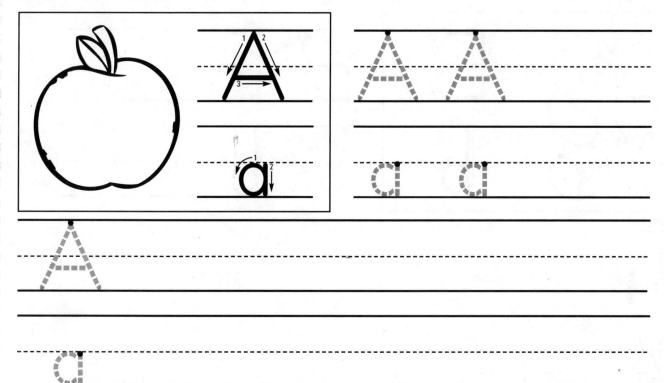

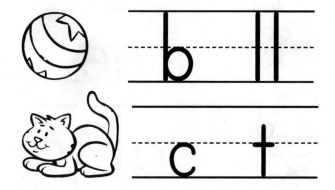  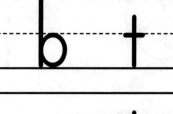

Fill in the blanks with **a**.

 b _ ll

b _ t

c _ t

_ nt

After the child has filled in the blanks in the activity below, ask him or her to use the picture clues to figure out each completed word.

B Is for Baby

Trace and write.

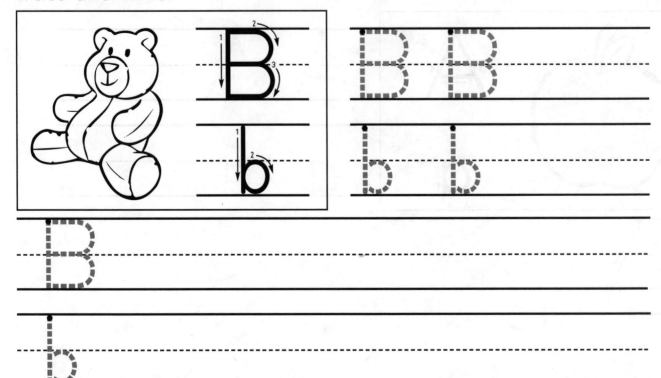

Fill in the blanks with **b**.

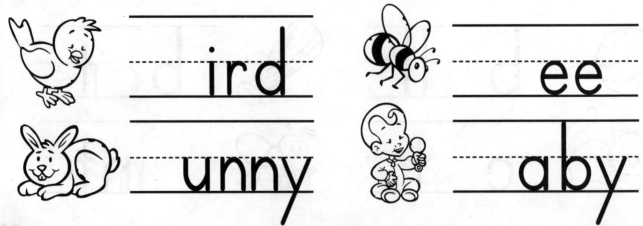

___ird

___ee

___unny

___aby

Printing **Bb**

After the child has filled in the blanks in the activity below, ask him or her to use the picture clues to figure out each completed word.

C Is for Cactus

Trace and write.

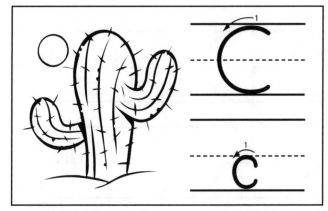

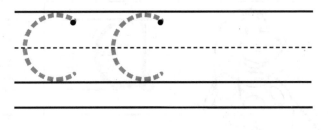

Fill in the blanks with **c**.

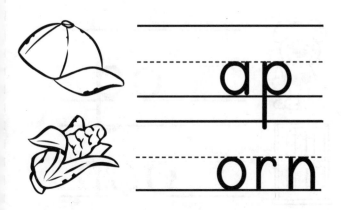

 ap

 ar

orn

 andy

After the child has filled in the blanks in the activity below, ask him or her to use the picture clues to figure out each completed word.

D Is for Dinosaur

Trace and write.

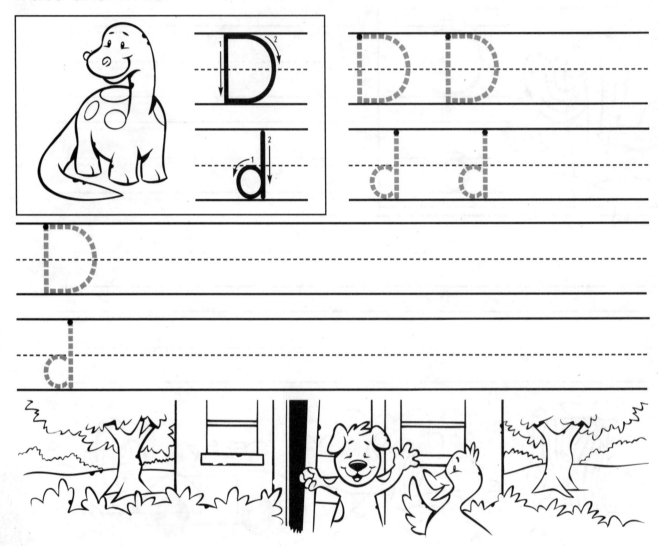

Fill in the blanks with **d**.

esk

oll

og

oor

After the child has filled in the blanks in the activity below, ask him or her to use the picture clues to figure out each completed word.

E Is for Elephant

Trace and write.

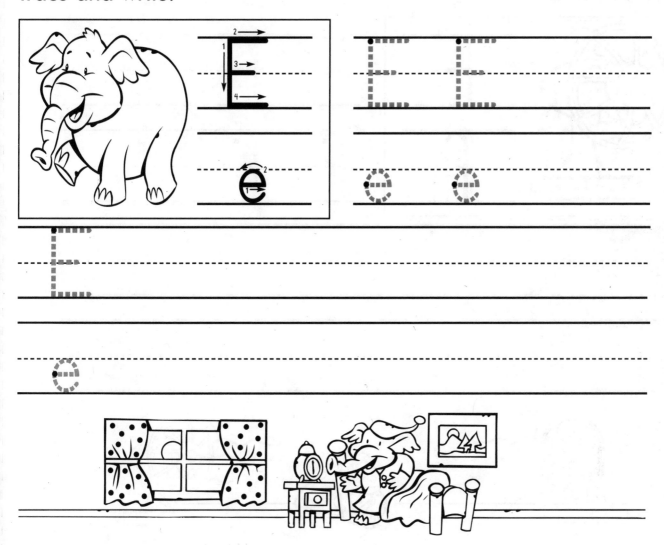

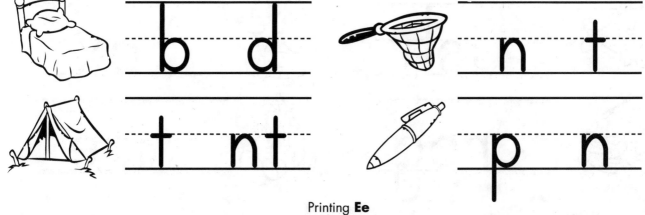

Fill in the blanks with **e**.

b___d   n___t

t___nt   p___n

After the child has filled in the blanks in the activity below, ask him or her to use the picture clues to figure out each completed word.

F Is for Fan

Trace and write.

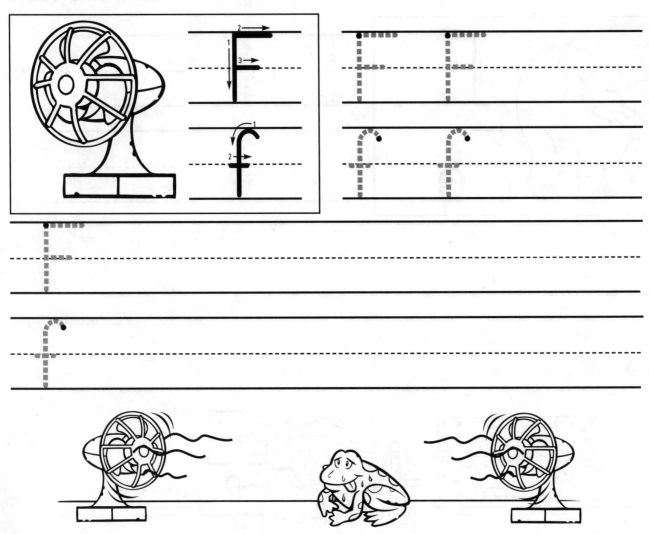

Fill in the blanks with **f**.

__ish

__ox

__rog

__ire

Printing **Ff**

After the child has filled in the blanks in the activity below, ask him or her to use the picture clues to figure out each completed word.

G Is for Goat

Trace and write.

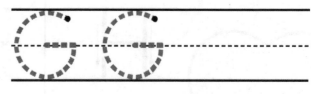

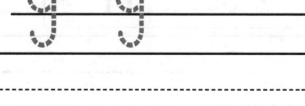

Fill in the blanks with **g**.

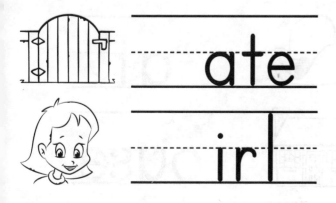

ate

irl

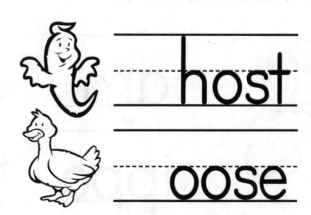

host

oose

After the child has filled in the blanks in the activity below, ask him or her to use the picture clues to figure out each completed word.

H Is for Heart

Trace and write.

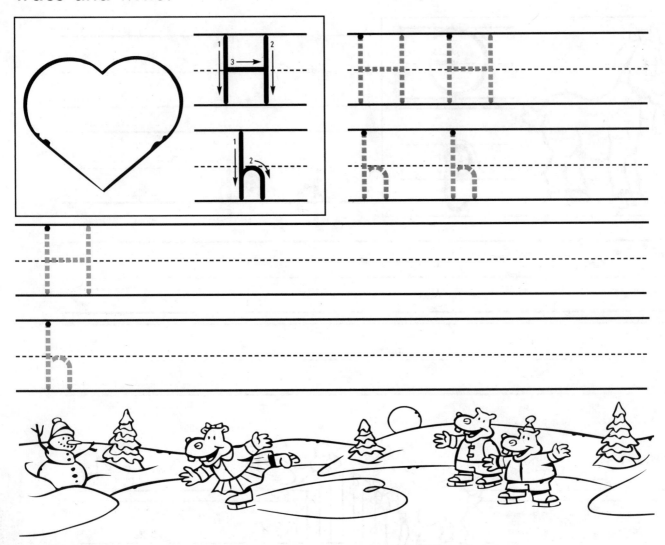

Fill in the blanks with **h**.

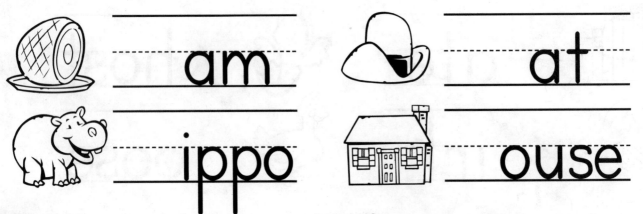

___am

___at

___ippo

___ouse

After the child has filled in the blanks in the activity below, ask him or her to use the picture clues to figure out each completed word.

I Is for Infant

Trace and write.

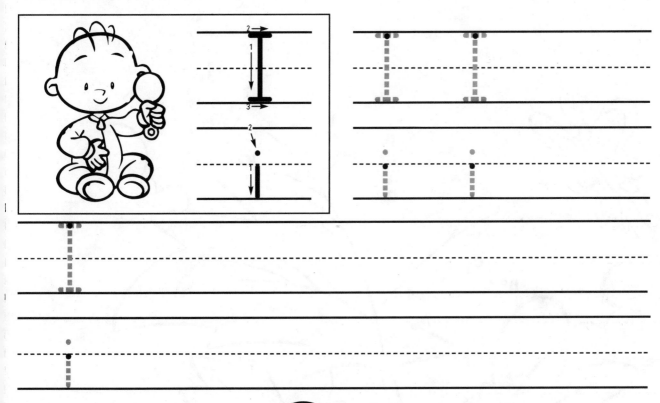

Fill in the blanks with **i**.

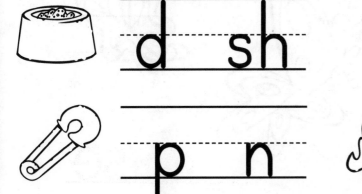

d___   sh___

qu___lt

p___n

w___g

Falling Leaves

Connect the dots from **A** to **L**. Color the picture.

Developing fine motor control

Ask the child to draw a path to help the family reach the end of the ride.

Roaring Roller Coaster

STOP

Developing fine motor control

227

A Nice Umbrella

Connect the dots from **M** to **U**. Color the picture.

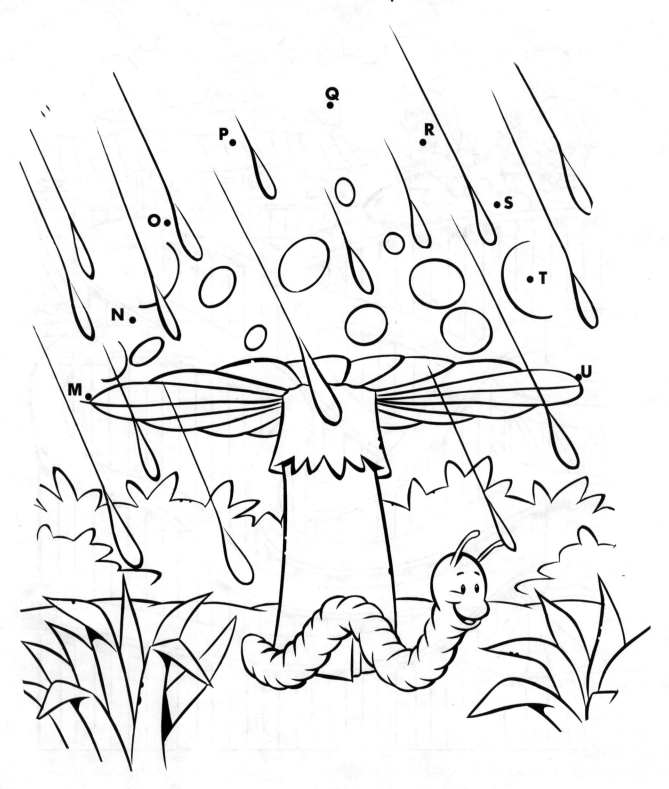

Developing fine motor control

After the child has filled in the blanks in the activity below, ask him or her to use the picture clues to figure out each completed word.

J Is for Juggler

Trace and write.

Fill in the blanks with **j**.

___ ar

___ ug

___ acks

___ acket

After the child has filled in the blanks in the activity below, ask him or her to use the picture clues to figure out each completed word.

K Is for Kangaroo

Trace and write.

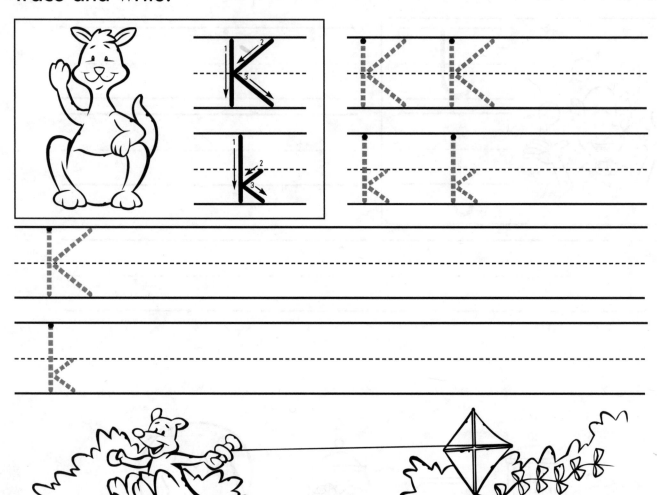

Fill in the blanks with **k**.

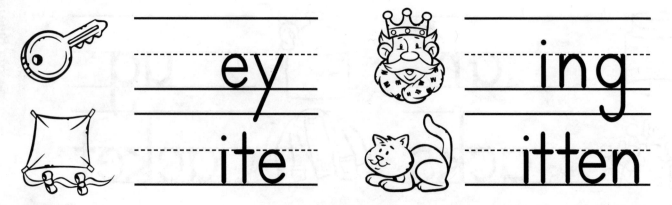

___ey

___ing

___ite

___itten

Printing **Kk**

After the child has filled in the blanks in the activity below, ask him or her to use the picture clues to figure out each completed word.

L Is for Leaf

Trace and write.

Fill in the blanks with **l**.

ake

amp

amb

og

After the child has copied the sentence below, read the sentence aloud to the child, pointing to each word.

M Is for Moon

Trace and write.

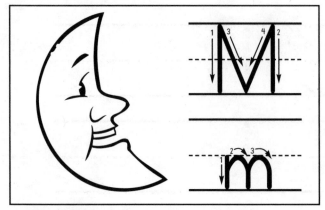
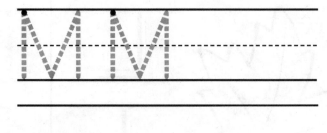

Copy the sentence below. You can make all the letters.

Meg made a meal.

Printing **Mm**

N Is for Nest

Trace and write.

Copy the sentence below. You can make all the letters.

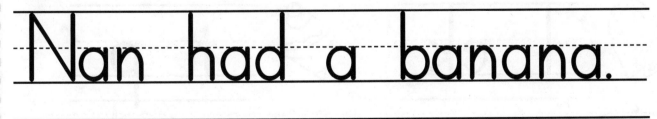

Nan had a banana.

Printing and Writing Practice

After the child has filled in the blanks in the activity below, ask him or her to use the picture clues to figure out each completed word.

O Is for Octopus

Trace and write.

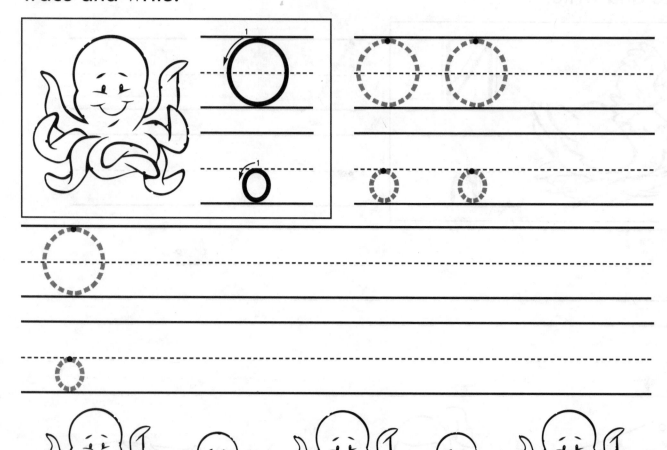

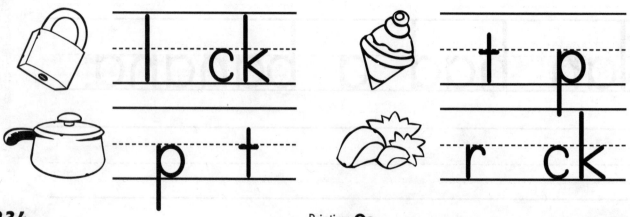

Fill in the blanks with **o**.

l___ck

___t___p

p___t

r___ck

P Is for Pencil

Trace and write.

Copy the sentence below. You can make all the letters.

Pam picks peppers.

After the child has filled in the blanks in the activity below, ask him or her to use the picture clues to figure out each completed word.

Q Is for Queen

Trace and write.

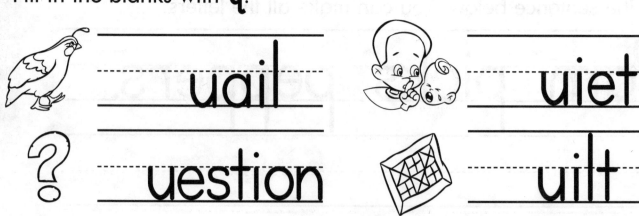

Fill in the blanks with **q**.

___uail

___uiet

___uestion

___uilt

R Is for Robot

Trace and write.

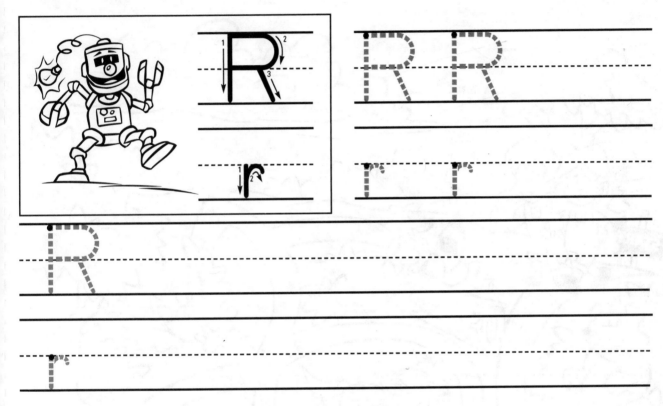

Copy the sentence below. You can make all the letters.

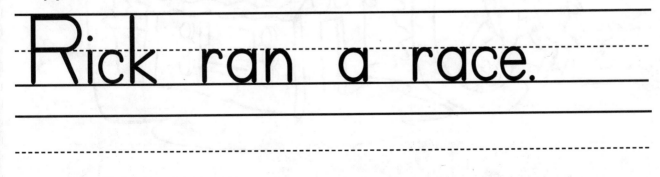

Rick ran a race.

Ask the child to draw a path for Hansel and Gretel to follow to the gingerbread house.

Helping Hansel and Gretel

Developing fine motor control

The King of Fruits

Connect the dots from **A** to **O**. Color the picture.

Down, Across and Slant

Trace and write.

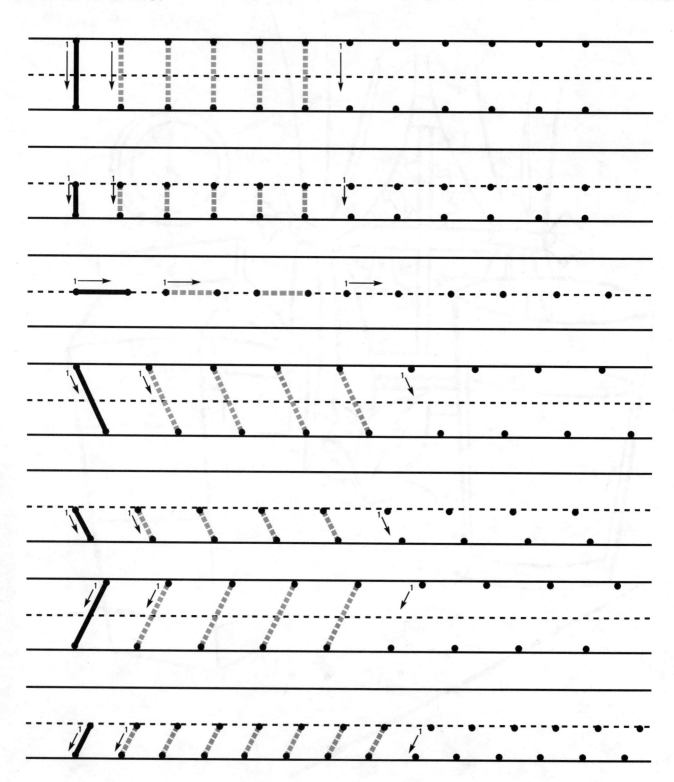

Forming straight strokes used in making letters

Circles and Curves

Trace and write.

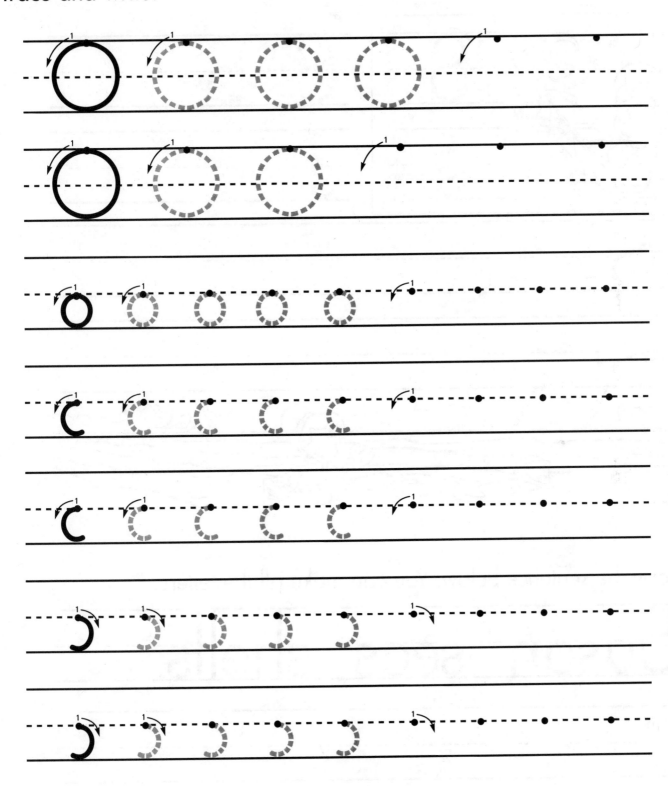

Printing and Writing Practice

After the child has copied the sentence below, read the sentence aloud to the child, pointing to each word.

S Is for Seesaw

Trace and write.

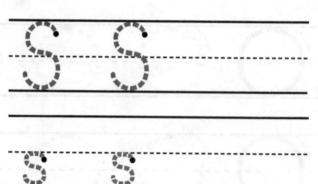

Copy the sentence below. You can make all the letters.

Susan sees shells.

After the child has copied the sentence below, read the sentence aloud to the child, pointing to each word.

T Is for Tractor

Trace and write.

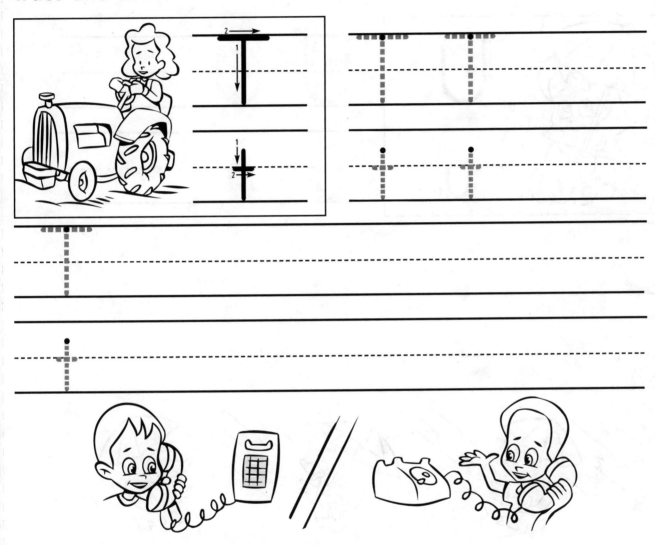

Copy the sentence below. You can make all the letters.

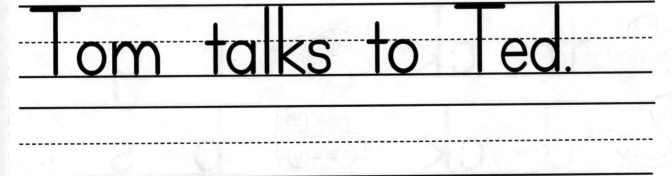

Tom talks to Ted.

After the child has filled in the blanks in the activity below, ask him or her to use the picture clues to figure out each completed word.

U Is for Umbrella

Trace and write.

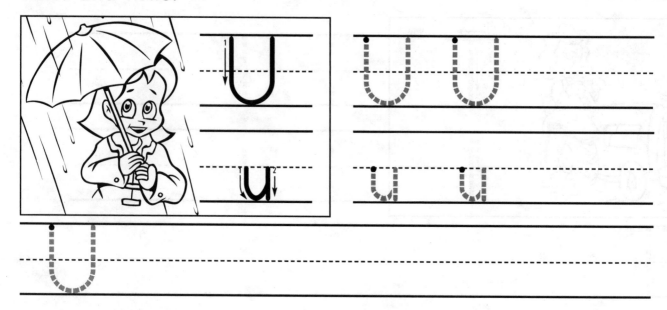

Fill in the blanks with **u**.

tr __ ck

d __ ck

r __ g

b __ s

Printing **Uu**

After the child has copied the sentence below, read the sentence aloud to the child, pointing to each word.

V Is for Valentine

Trace and write.

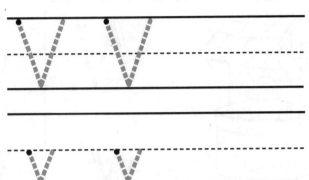

Copy the sentence below. You can make all the letters.

Val drives a van.

W Is for Well

Trace and write.

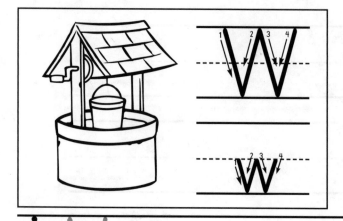

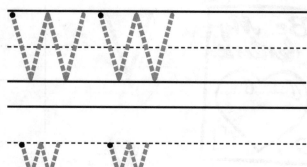

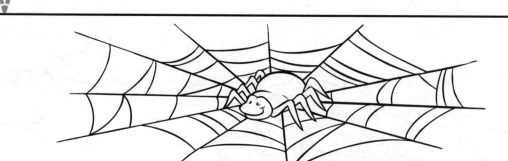

Copy the sentence below. You can make all the letters.

Wes saw a web.

Three Slant-line Letters

Trace and write.

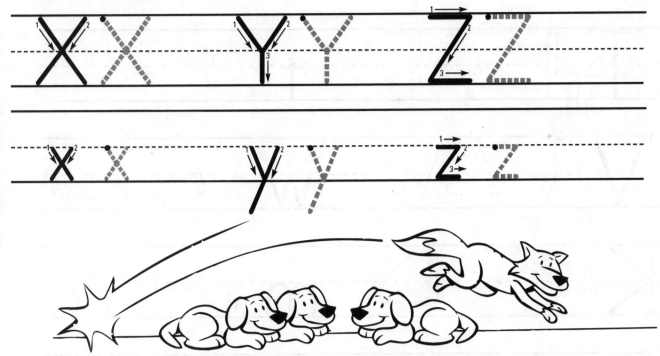

Read the sentence below. You can make all the letters.

The quick brown fox

jumped over lazy dogs.

Printing and Writing Practice

Get It Together

Trace and write.

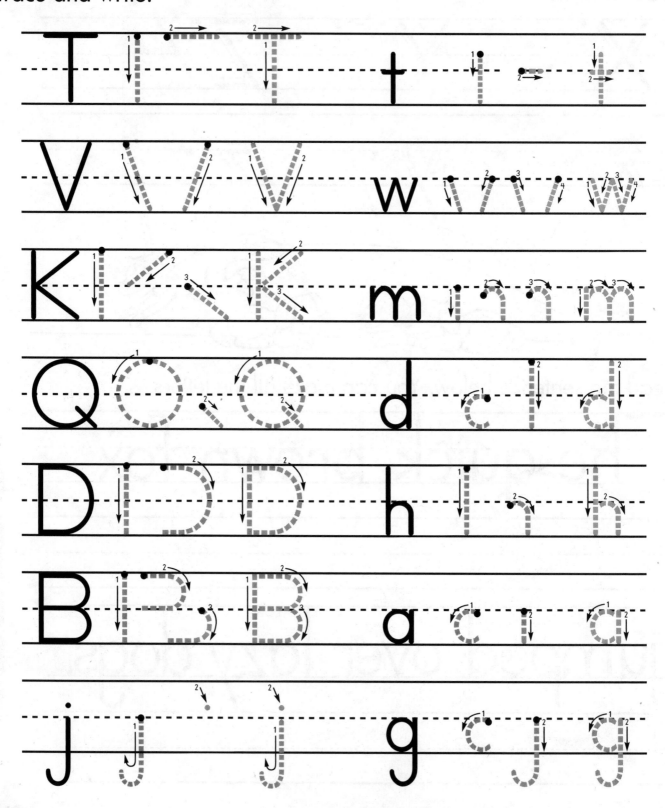

Forming letters

Winter Days

Connect the dots from **A** to **Z**.

Answer Key

As the child completes the pages in this section, review his or her answers. When you take the time to correct the work and explain mistakes, you're showing your child that you feel learning is important.

page 217

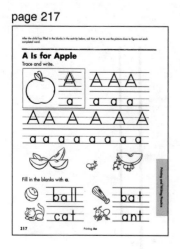

page 218

page 219

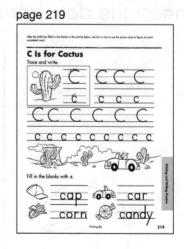

page 220

page 221

page 222

page 223

page 224

page 225

page 226

Falling Leaves
Connect the dots from **A** to **L**. Color the picture.

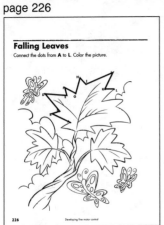

226   Developing fine motor control

page 227

Ask the child to draw a path to help the family reach the end of the ride.

Roaring Roller Coaster

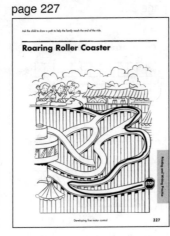

Developing fine motor control   227

page 228

A Nice Umbrella
Connect the dots from **M** to **U**. Color the picture.

228   Developing fine motor control

page 229

After the child has filled in the blanks in the activity below, ask him or her to use the picture clues to figure out each completed word.

J Is for Juggler
Trace and write.

Fill in the blanks with **j**.

jar
jacks
jug
jacket

Printing Jj   229

page 230

After the child has filled in the blanks in the activity below, ask him or her to use the picture clues to figure out each completed word.

K Is for Kangaroo
Trace and write.

Fill in the blanks with **k**.

key
kite
king
kitten

230   Printing Kk

page 231

After the child has filled in the blanks in the activity below, ask him or her to use the picture clues to figure out each completed word.

L Is for Leaf
Trace and write.

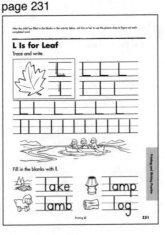

Fill in the blanks with **l**.

lake
lamb
lamp
log

Printing Ll   231

page 232

After the child has copied the sentence below, read the sentence aloud to the child, pointing to each word.

M Is for Moon
Trace and write.

Copy the sentence below. You can make all the letters.

Meg made a meal.
Meg made a meal.

232   Printing Mm

page 233

After the child has copied the sentence below, read the sentence aloud to the child, pointing to each word.

N Is for Nest.
Trace and write.

Copy the sentence below. You can make all the letters.

Nan had a banana.
Nan had a banana.

Printing Nn   233

page 234

After the child has filled in the blanks in the activity below, ask him or her to use the picture clues to figure out each completed word.

O Is for Octopus
Trace and write.

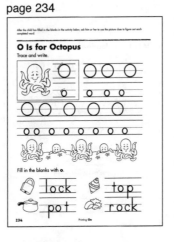

Fill in the blanks with **o**.

lock
pot
top
rock

234   Printing Oo

page 235

After the child has copied the sentence below, read the sentence aloud to the child, pointing to each word.

P Is for Pencil
Trace and write.

Copy the sentence below. You can make all the letters.

Pam picks peppers.
Pam picks peppers.

Printing Pp   235

page 236

After the child has filled in the blanks in the activity below, ask him or her to use the picture clues to figure out each completed word.

Q Is for Queen
Trace and write.

Fill in the blanks with **q**.

quail
question
quiet
quilt

236   Printing Qq

page 237

After the child has copied the sentence below, read the sentence aloud to the child, pointing to each word.

R Is for Robot
Trace and write.

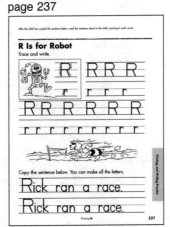

Copy the sentence below. You can make all the letters.

Rick ran a race.
Rick ran a race.

Printing Rr   237

Printing and Writing Practice

page 238

Ask the child to draw a path for Hansel and Gretel to follow to the gingerbread house.

Helping Hansel and Gretel

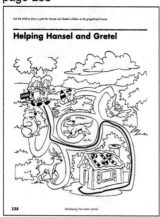

238　　Developing fine motor control

page 239

The King of Fruits
Connect the dots from **A** to **O**. Color the picture.

Developing fine motor control; understanding alphabet order　239

page 240

Down, Across and Slant
Trace and write.

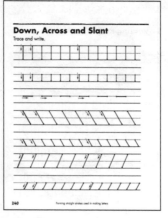

240　　Forming straight strokes used in making letters

page 241

Circles and Curves
Trace and write.

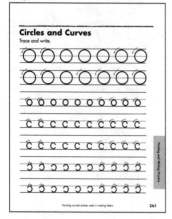

Forming curved strokes used in making letters　241

page 242

After the child has copied the sentence below, read the sentence aloud to the child, pointing to each word.

S Is for Seesaw
Trace and write.

Copy the sentence below. You can make all the letters.

Susan sees shells.
Susan sees shells.

242　　Printing Ss

page 243

After the child has copied the sentence below, read the sentence aloud to the child, pointing to each word.

T Is for Tractor
Trace and write.

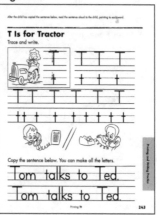

Copy the sentence below. You can make all the letters.

Tom talks to Ted.
Tom talks to Ted.

Printing Tt　243

page 244

After the child has filled in the blanks in the activity below, ask him or her to use the picture clues to figure out each completed word.

U Is for Umbrella
Trace and write.

Fill in the blanks with **u**.

truck　rug
duck　bus

244　　Printing Uu

page 245

After the child has copied the sentence below, read the sentence aloud to the child, pointing to each word.

V Is for Valentine
Trace and write.

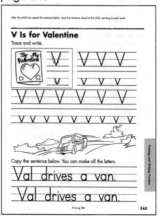

Copy the sentence below. You can make all the letters.

Val drives a van.
Val drives a van.

Printing Vv　245

page 246

After the child has copied the sentence below, read the sentence aloud to the child, pointing to each word.

W Is for Well
Trace and write.

Copy the sentence below. You can make all the letters.

Wes saw a web.
Wes saw a web.

246　　Printing Ww

page 247

After the child has copied the sentence below, read the sentence aloud to the child, pointing to each word.

Three Slant-line Letters
Trace and write.

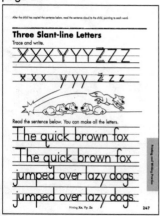

Read the sentence below. You can make all the letters.

The quick brown fox
The quick brown fox
jumped over lazy dogs.
jumped over lazy dogs.

Printing Xx, Yy, Zz　247

page 248

Get It Together
Trace and write.

248　　Forming letters

page 249

Winter Days
Connect the dots from **A** to **Z**.

Developing fine motor control; understanding alphabet order　249

Ask the child to circle the animal in each row that is facing a different direction.

Direction?

Developing visual discrimination; directionality

253

Ask the child to circle the thing in each row that is facing a different direction.

Wrong Way

Developing visual discrimination; directionality

Encourage the child to use the words *first*, *next*, and *last* to tell a story about the pictures at the top of the page. Then help the child cut out the pictures at the bottom of page 257. Ask him or her to paste them in logical order at the bottom of the page and then tell the raccoon's story using the words *first*, *next*, and *last*.

In the Swim

Understanding story sequence; telling a story using first, next, and last

Help the child cut out the pictures of the girl eating the banana on the top of page 257. Ask the child to put the pictures in logical order, and paste them in the first row of boxes labeled "first," "next," and "last." Then ask the child to cut out the pictures of the boy roller skating and repeat the process in the next row.

Eating and Skating

first   next   last

first   next   last

Understanding story sequence; telling a story using first, next, and last

Use on pages 255 and 256

Understanding story sequence; telling a story using first, next, and last

Ask the child to color the thing in each row that faces a different direction.

Wrong Way at the Beach

Developing visual discrimination; directionality

Ask the child to circle the thing in each row that is going in a different direction.

Toy Turn-Around

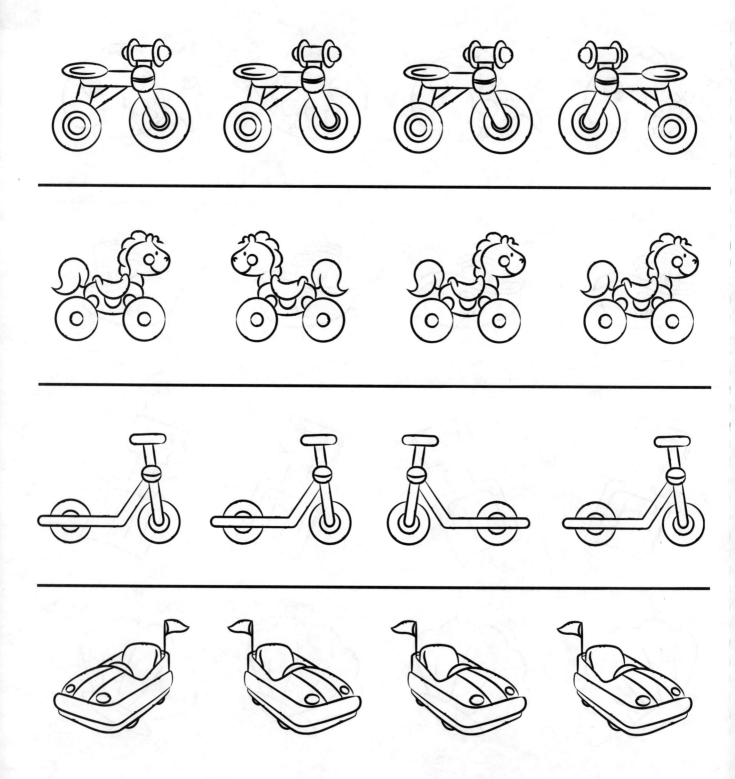

Developing visual discrimination; directionality

Ask the child to point to the rabbit with an empty glass and then to the rabbit with a full glass. Point to the words *empty* and *full*. Explain that they are called opposites. Then say, "Color the empty popcorn box red. Color the full box of popcorn yellow."

Empty and Full

empty

full

Color the **empty** box **red** .

Color the **full** box **yellow** .

Understanding opposites

Ask the child to tell you whether the large nest is full or empty. Ask, "What's the opposite of empty? Color the small nest that shows the opposite." Then ask the child to color the toy box that is the opposite of full.

More Empty and Full

empty

full

empty

full

full

empty

Understanding opposites

Ask the child to tell about the first picture in each row. Point out and read the word under each picture. Then ask the child to circle the picture that show its opposite.

Opposites Review

happy

out

full

Understanding opposites

[1] Explain to the child that each row of three pictures on the page shows a story, but that the pictures are mixed up.
[2] Look at the first row and help the child to figure out the story. Then have him or her tell which picture should come first, which should come next and which should come last. Help the child to read the words *first, next* and *last* below each picture and then circle the correct word for each picture.

Mixed-up Stories

first   next   last

first   next   last

first   next   last

first   next   last

first   next   last

first   next   last

    Understanding story sequence; telling a story using first, next, and last

1] Explain to the child that each row of three pictures on the page shows a story, but that the pictures are mixed up.
[2] Look at the first row, and help the child figure out the story. Then have him or her tell which picture should come first, which should come next and which should come last. Help the child read the words *first*, *next* and *last* below each picture and then circle the correct word for each picture.

More Mixed-up Stories

first   next   last   first   next   last   first   next   last

first   next   last   first   next   last   first   next   last

Understanding story sequence; telling a story using first, next, and last

Ask the child to circle the objects that belong in the toy box.

Toys

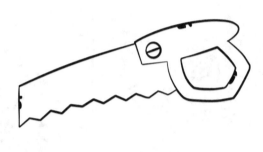

Classifying objects

Ask the child to color all the things that belong in the tool box.

Tools

Color all the things that belong in the .

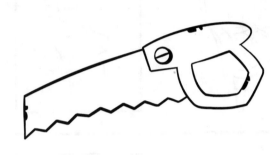

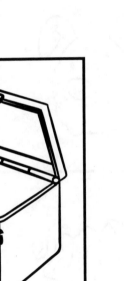

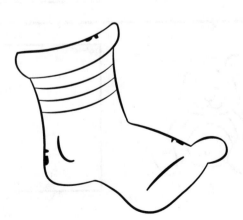

Ask the child to look carefully at the pictures in each row and tell how they are alike. Turn to page 271 and help the child find, cut out, and paste the pictures that belong in the empty boxes at the ends of the rows.

What Goes Where?

Classifying objects

Ask the child to look carefully at the pictures in each row and tell how they are alike. Turn to page 271 and help the child find, cut out, and paste the pictures that belong in the empty boxes at the ends of the rows.

Grouping

Classifying objects

Ask the child to look carefully at the pictures in each row and tell how they are alike. Turn to page 271 and help the child find, cut out, and paste the pictures that belong in the empty boxes at the ends of the rows.

What's Alike?

Classifying objects

Cut-outs

Use on page 268.

Use on page 269.

Use on page 270.

Ask the child to point to the box that is open and then to the box that is closed. Point to the words *open* and *closed*. Explain that they are called opposites. Then ask the child to look at the picture of the kittens having a picnic and say, "Color the open lunchbox green. Color the closed lunchbox red."

Open and Closed

open   **closed**

Color the **open** lunchbox green

Color the **closed** lunchbox red

Understanding opposites   **273**

Discuss whether the large book is open or closed. Ask, "What is the opposite of closed? Color the picture that shows the opposite." Repeat for the doors. Point out the words *open* and *closed* below the pictures.

More Open and Closed

closed

closed

open

open

closed

open

Ask the child to point to the bear that is down the ladder and then to the bear that is up. Point to the words *up* and *down*. Explain that they are called opposites. Then say "Color the balloon that is up yellow. Color the balloon that is down blue. Then color the rest of the picture."

Up and Down

up

down

Color the balloon that is **up** (((yellow)=o .

Color the balloon that is **down** ((blue)=o .

Discuss whether the bird is up or down. Ask, "What is the opposite of up? Color the picture that shows the opposite." Repeat for the planes. Point out the words *up* and *down* below the pictures.

More Up and Down

up

up

down

up

up

down

Understanding opposites

Ask the child to point to the front of the car and then to the back. Point to the words *front* and *back*. Explain that they are called opposites. Then say, "Color the toy soldier with his front to us blue. Color the toy soldier with his back to us red. Then color the rest of the picture."

Front and Back

front   **back**

Color the toy soldier with his **front** to us blue .

Color the toy soldier with his **back** to us red .

Understanding opposites

277

Discuss whether you can see the front or the back of the rabbit on the left. Ask, "What is the opposite of front? Color the picture that shows the opposite." Repeat for the kangaroos. Point out the words *front* and *back* below the pictures.

More Front and Back

front   **front**   **back**

front   **front**   **back**

278   Understanding opposites

Opposite Review II

Color the **opposite**.

closed

down

back

Understanding opposites

Food

Color all the things that belong in the .

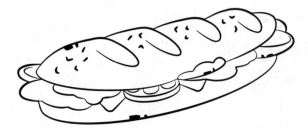

Classifying objects

Ask the child to color all the animals that belong on the farm.

Farm Animals

Color all the things that belong on the .

Classifying objects

281

Answer Key

As the child completes the pages in this section, review his or her answers. When you take the time to correct the work and explain mistakes, you're showing your child that you feel learning is important.

page 253

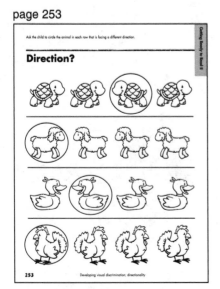

page 254

page 255

page 256

page 259

page 260

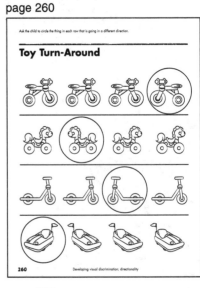

page 261

page 262

page 263

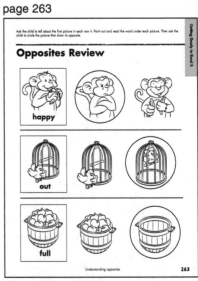

page 264

page 265

page 266

page 267

page 268

page 269

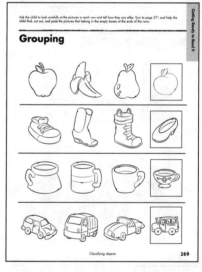

page 270

page 273

page 274

Answers

page 275

page 276

page 277

page 278

page 279

page 280

page 281

Ask the child to follow these directions: [1] Draw a nose on the clown. [2] Draw buttons on the clown. [3] Draw a hat on the clown. [4] Color the picture.

Clowning Around

Point to the incomplete cat picture and ask the child to follow these directions: [1] Draw eyes on the cat. [2] Draw a nose on the cat. [3] Draw whiskers on the cat. [4] Draw a tail on the cat.

Here, Kitty!

Following directions

Encourage the child to talk about the bear's features and discuss his or her own features. Then ask the child to fill in the blank face by drawing his or her own. At the bottom of the page, help the child to write his or her name.

My Picture

My name is _____ .

Developing self-awareness

287

Ask the child to draw the number of candles on the cake that reflects his or her age, then read the sentences below aloud and help the child to fill in the blanks.

My Birthday

I am _____ years old.

My birthday is on _____ .

Developing self-awareness

Ask the child to circle his or her favorite kind of pet. Then read the sentence below aloud and ask the child to fill in the blank.

My Favorite Pets

rabbit

dog

cat

fish

gerbil

bird

My favorite pet is _____ .

Ask the child to trace his or her hand in the space below. Then read the sentence below aloud and ask the child to fill in the blank.

My Hands

I have ＿＿＿＿＿ fingers on each hand.

Developing self-awareness

Ask the child to trace his or her foot in the space below. Then read the sentence below aloud and ask the child to fill in the blank.

My Feet

I have_____toes on each foot.

Developing self-awareness

Explain that people have five senses that they use daily—touch, taste, smell, hearing and sight. Ask the child to draw a line from each picture on the left to the item that goes with it on the right.

Ready for School

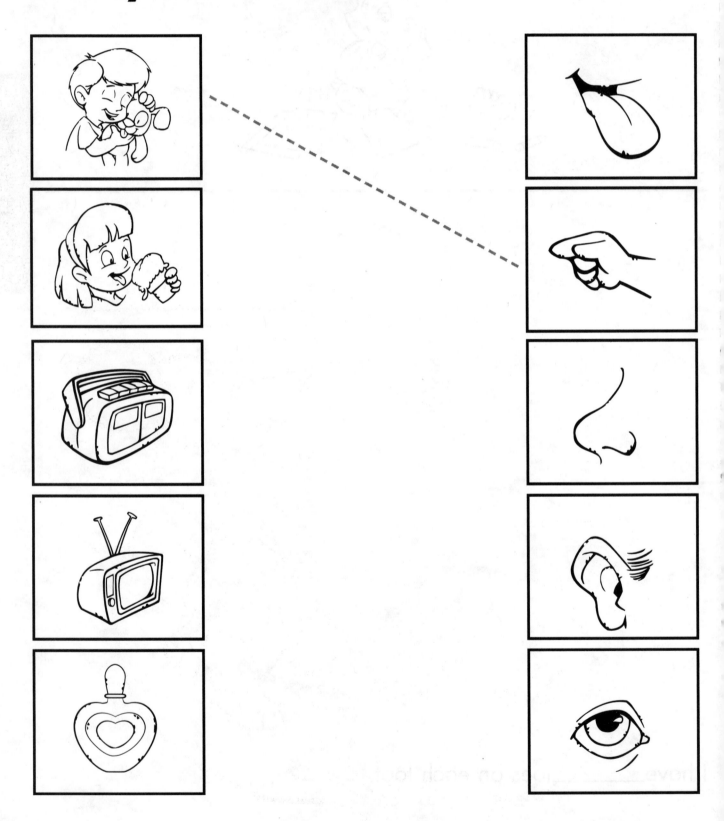

Understanding the senses; matching

I Can See

Color 1 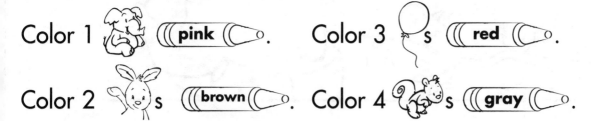 pink .   Color 3 s red .

Color 2 s brown .   Color 4 s gray .

Then color the rest of the picture.

Understanding the senses; recognizing differences (visual discrimination)

Ask the child to color the pictures and then circle the objects that make noise.

I Can Hear

Understanding the senses

Ask the child to color the pictures and then circle the objects that someone can smell.

I Can Smell

Understanding the senses

295

Ask the child to color the pictures and then circle the objects that someone can touch.

I Can Touch

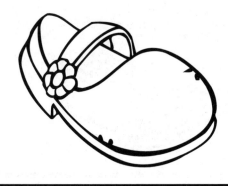

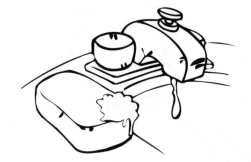

Ask the child to color the pictures and then circle the objects that someone can taste.

I Can Taste

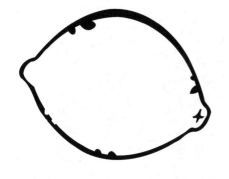

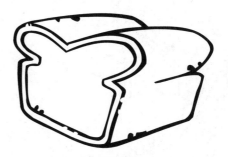

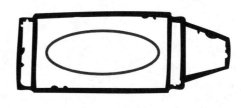

Understanding the senses

Discuss times when the child has been happy and other times when the child has been sad. Ask the child to look at each picture and then circle one of the two faces below that shows how he or she would feel in each situation.

How I Would Feel

Developing self-awareness: feelings

Ask the child to look at each picture and then circle one of the two faces below that shows how he or she would feel in each situation.

Happy or Sad?

Developing self-awareness: feelings

Discuss times when the child has felt angry and other times when the child has felt surprised. Ask the child to look at each picture and then circle one of the two faces below that shows how he or she would feel in each situation.

Angry or Surprised I

Developing self-awareness: feelings

Ask the child to look at each picture and then circle one of the two faces below that shows how he or she would feel in each situation.

Angry or Surprised II

Developing self-awareness: feelings

301

Discuss all the different kinds of places where people can live. Then ask the child to complete the dot-to-dot. Say, "Every place that people live has an address that tells other people where the home is located." Help the child write his or her address on the line provided and then read the sentence aloud together.

My Home

My address is

Developing self-awareness: address

My Phone Number

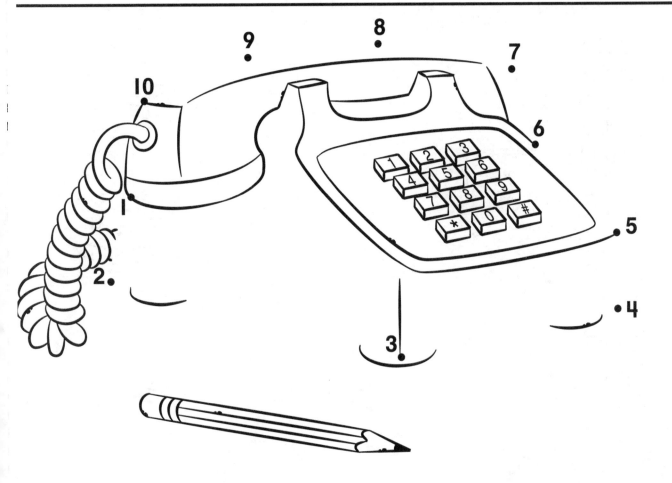

My phone number is

Talk about the work of each person in the left column. Ask the child to draw a line from each person to the item in the right column that he or she needs for the job.

What Do They Use?

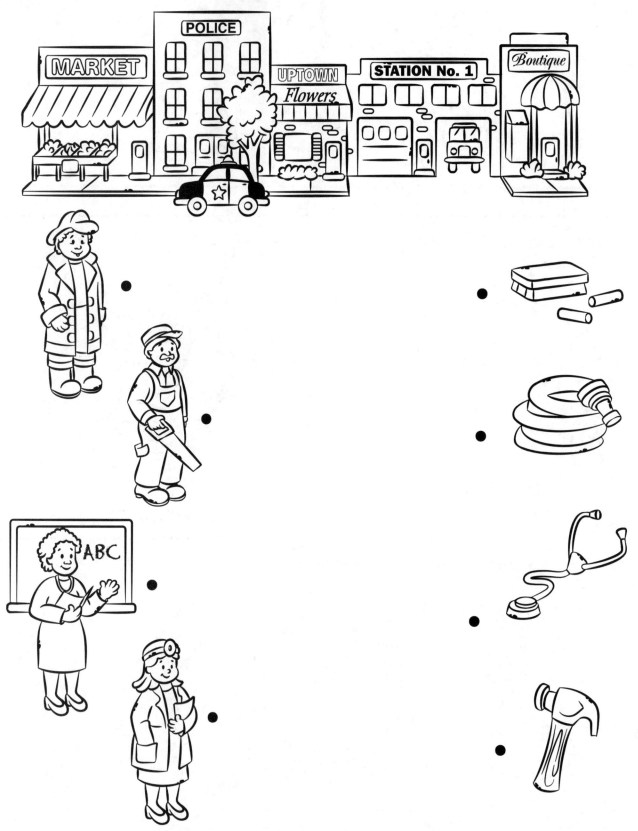

Developing community awareness

Point to each picture at the top of the page and help the child read its name. Explain that those names rhyme because they both have the –at sound at the end. Then help the child complete the rest of the page.

-at Rhymes

cat

hat

Color the one that rhymes with **cat**.

Color the two that have rhyming names.

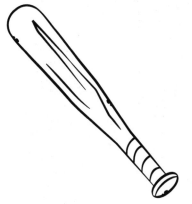

Point to each picture at the top of the page and help the child read its name. Explain that those names rhyme because they both have the *–ock* sound at the end. Then help the child complete the rest of the page.

-ock Rhymes

clock   **sock**

Color the one that rhymes with **clock**.

Color the two that have rhyming names.

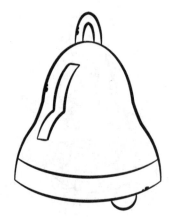

Identifying words that rhyme

-an Rhymes

man

can

Color the one that rhymes with **can**.

Color the two that have rhyming names.

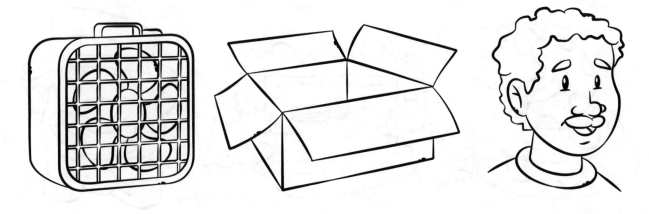

-ake Rhymes

cake

lake

Color the one that rhymes with **cake**.

Color the two that have rhyming names.

Identifying words that rhyme

Point to each picture at the top of the page and help the child read its name. Explain that those names rhyme because they both have the *–am* sound at the end. Then help the child complete the rest of the page.

-am Rhymes

ram

jam

Color the one that rhymes with **ram**.

Color the two that have rhyming names.

Identifying words that rhyme

Ready for School

309

-en Rhymes

pen

ten

Color the one that rhymes with **pen**.

Color the two that have rhyming names.

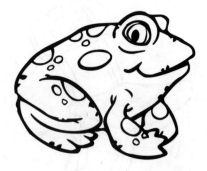

Identifying words that rhyme

Point to each picture at the top of the page and help the child read its name. Explain that those names rhyme because they both have the long e sound at the end. Then help the child complete the rest of the page.

Long e Rhymes

tree

bee

Color the one that rhymes with **bee**.

Color the two that have rhyming names.

Identifying words that rhyme

-um Rhymes

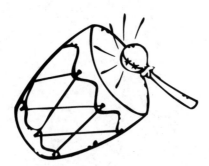

drum   **plum**

Color the one that rhymes with **drum**.

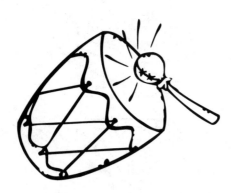

Color the two that have rhyming names.

Identifying words that rhyme

Point to each picture at the top of the page and help the child read its name. Explain that those names rhyme because they both have the *-ing* sound at the end. Then help the child complete the rest of the page.

-ing Rhymes

king

ring

Color the one that rhymes with **king**.

Color the two that have rhyming names.

Point to each picture at the top of the page and help the child read its name. Explain that those names rhyme because they both have the *-ug* sound at the end. Then help the child complete the rest of the page.

-ug Rhymes

bug

mug

Color the one that rhymes with **bug**.

Color the two that have rhyming names.

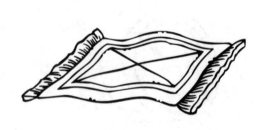

Identifying words that rhyme

Point to each picture at the top of the page and help the child read its name. Explain that those names rhym[e]
they both have the –ed sound at the end. Then help the child complete the rest of the page.

-ed Rhymes

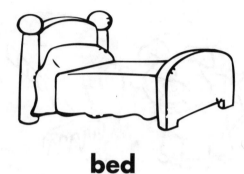

bed

sled

Color the one that rhymes with **bed**.

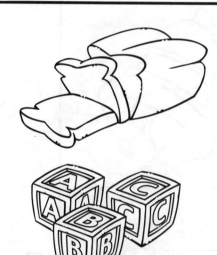

Color the two that have rhyming names.

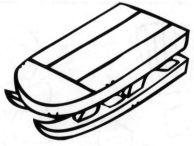

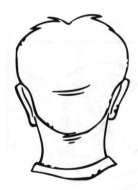

Identifying words that rhyme

Ready for School

Remind [...]
first p[...]
rh[...]

315

...he child that rhyming words, such as *look/book* and *man/can*, sound alike. Ask the child to say the name of the
...cture in each row and color it. Then ask him or her to name the rest of the pictures in each row and say "Which ones
...me with the first picture? Circle those pictures."

Rhyme Time

Identifying words that rhyme

Ask the child to say the name of the first picture in each row and color it. Then ask him or her to name the rest of the pictures in each row and say, "Which names rhyme with the first picture? Circle those pictures."

More Rhyme Time

Identifying words that rhyme

317

Answer Key

As the child completes the pages in this section, review his or her answers. When you take the time to correct the work and explain mistakes, you're showing your child that you feel learning is important.

page 285

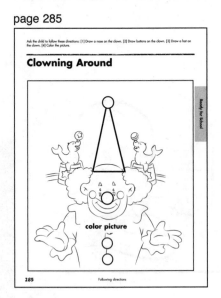

page 286

page 292

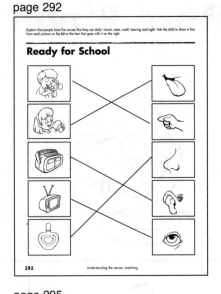

page 293

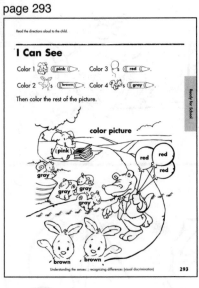

page 294

page 295

page 296

page 297

page 298

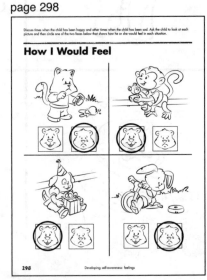

page 299

Ask the child to look at each picture and then circle one of the two faces below that shows how he or she would feel in each situation.

Happy or Sad?

Developing self-awareness: feelings   299

page 300

Discuss times when the child has felt angry and other times when the child has felt surprised. Ask the child to look at each picture and then circle one of the two faces below that shows how he or she would feel in each situation.

Angry or Surprised I

300   Developing self-awareness: feelings

page 301

Ask the child to look at each picture and then circle one of the two faces below that shows how he or she would feel in each situation.

Angry or Surprised II

Developing self-awareness: feelings   301

page 302

Discuss all the different kinds of places where people can live. Then ask the child to complete the dot-to-dot. Say, "Every place that people live has an address that tells other people where the home is located." Help the child write his or her address on the line provided and then read the sentence aloud together.

My Home

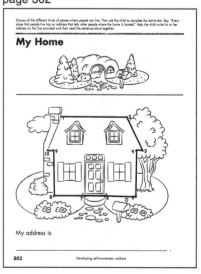

My address is

302   Developing self-awareness: address

page 303

Ask the child to complete the dot-to-dot. Then say, "Every phone has a number so people can call it from other phones." Help the child write his or her phone number and then read the sentence aloud.

My Phone Number

My phone number is

Developing self-awareness: phone number   303

page 304

Talk about the work of each person in the left column. Ask the child to draw a line from each person to the item in the right column that he or she needs for the job.

What Do They Use?

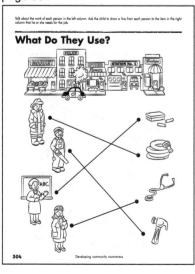

304   Developing community awareness

page 305

Point to each picture at the top of the page and help the child read its name. Explain that those names rhyme because they both have the -at sound at the end. Then help the child complete the rest of the page.

-at Rhymes

cat   hat

Color the one that rhymes with **cat**.

Color the two that have rhyming names.

Identifying words that rhyme   305

page 306

Point to each picture at the top of the page and help the child read its name. Explain that those names rhyme because they both have the -ock sound at the end. Then help the child complete the rest of the page.

-ock Rhymes

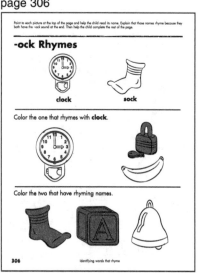

clock   sock

Color the one that rhymes with **clock**.

Color the two that have rhyming names.

306   Identifying words that rhyme

page 307

Point to each picture at the top of the page and help the child read its name. Explain that those names rhyme because they both have the -an sound at the end. Then help the child complete the rest of the page.

-an Rhymes

man   can

Color the one that rhymes with **can**.

Color the two that have rhyming names.

Identifying words that rhyme   307

Ready for School

page 308

Point to each picture at the top of the page and help the child read its name. Explain that those names rhyme because they both have the -ake sound at the end. Then help the child complete the rest of the page.

-ake Rhymes

cake   lake

Color the one that rhymes with **cake**.

Color the two that have rhyming names.

308   Identifying words that rhyme

page 309

Point to each picture at the top of the page and help the child read its name. Explain that those names rhyme because they both have the -am sound at the end. Then help the child complete the rest of the page.

-am Rhymes

ram   jam

Color the one that rhymes with **ram**.

Color the two that have rhyming names.

Identifying words that rhyme   309

page 310

Point to each picture at the top of the page and help the child read its name. Explain that those names rhyme because they both have the -en sound at the end. Then help the child complete the rest of the page.

-en Rhymes

pen   ten

Color the one that rhymes with **pen**.

Color the two that have rhyming names.

310   Identifying words that rhyme

page 311

Point to each picture at the top of the page and help the child read its name. Explain that those names rhyme because they both have the long e sound at the end. Then help the child complete the rest of the page.

Long E Rhymes

tree   bee

Color the one that rhymes with **bee**.

Color the two that have rhyming names.

Identifying words that rhyme   311

page 312

Point to each picture at the top of the page and help the child read its name. Explain that those names rhyme because they both have the -um sound at the end. Then help the child complete the rest of the page.

-um Rhymes

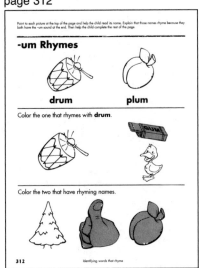

drum   plum

Color the one that rhymes with **drum**.

Color the two that have rhyming names.

312   Identifying words that rhyme

page 313

Point to each picture at the top of the page and help the child read its name. Explain that those names rhyme because they both have the -ing sound at the end. Then help the child complete the rest of the page.

-ing Rhymes

king   ring

Color the one that rhymes with **king**.

Color the two that have rhyming names.

Identifying words that rhyme   313

page 314

Point to each picture at the top of the page and help the child read its name. Explain that those names rhyme because they both have the -ug sound at the end. Then help the child complete the rest of the page.

-ug Rhymes

bug   mug

Color the one that rhymes with **bug**.

Color the two that have rhyming names.

314   Identifying words that rhyme

page 315

Point to each picture at the top of the page and help the child read its name. Explain that those names rhyme because they both have the -ed sound at the end. Then help the child complete the rest of the page.

-ed Rhymes

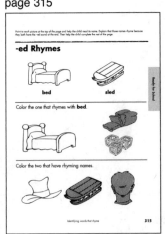

bed   sled

Color the one that rhymes with **bed**.

Color the two that have rhyming names.

Identifying words that rhyme   315

page 316

Remind the child that rhyming words, such as look/book and man/can, sound alike. Ask the child to say the name of the first picture in each row and color it. Then ask him or her to name the rest of the pictures in each row and say "Which names rhyme with the first picture? Circle those pictures."

Rhyme Time

316   Identifying words that rhyme

page 317

Ask the child to say the name of the first picture in each row and color it. Then ask him or her to name the rest of the pictures in each row and say "Which names rhyme with the first picture? Circle those pictures."

More Rhyme Time

Identifying words that rhyme   317

320   Answers